MW00581177

ANTIQUE AND UNUSUAL THIMBLES

MON COEUR

DÉVOUÉ À VOUS

ANTIQUE AND UNUSUAL THIMBLES

Jo Anne Rath

South Brunswick and New York: A. S. Barnes and Company
London: Thomas Yoseloff Ltd.

A. S. Barnes and Co., Inc.
Cranbury, New Jersey 08512

Thomas Yoseloff Ltd
Magdalen House
136-148 Tooley Street
London SE1 2TT, England

Library of Congress Cataloging in Publication Data

Rath, Jo Anne, 1947-
Antique and unusual thimbles.

Bibliography: p.
Includes index.
1. Thimbles–Collectors and collecting.
I. Title.
NK9505.7.R37 1978 646.1'9 76-57474
ISBN 0-498-02065-7

PRINTED IN THE UNITED STATES OF AMERICA

To
Madeline Rath,
who started my collection,
and
Patricia Pierce,
who helped it grow

CONTENTS

ACKNOWLEDGMENTS

I gratefully thank the following people without whose help this book could not have been written: Patricia Pierce; Elizabeth Bassett; Janice Dyer; Colonial Williamsburg–Williamsburg, Virginia; The Newark Museum–Newark, New Jersey; Pier Street Antiques–Wall, New Jersey; A La Viellie Russie–New York, New York.

INTRODUCTION

WHEN people hear that the author collects thimbles, they immediately conclude that she is crazy. That is because most people, when they think of thimbles, think of the ordinary steel thimble that can be found, three different sizes to a card, in the five-and-ten-cent store. But when they see a collection of antique thimbles they are amazed at the variety of designs and the beauty that thimbles can have. Their first question is: "Where do you get them?" The answer is: "From family and friends, from haunting antique shows, and finding dealers who specialize in such items and will keep you in mind when they find a special one." The next question is: "How did you get started?" In the author's case there were two main reasons: illness kept her inactive for a period of time, and she looked for a hobby that was inexpensive and took up little space. The first thimble in the collection was one with a scene that had belonged to the author's grandmother's twin sister, who died as a young girl. It was passed down from grandmother, to mother, to the author.

In a very short time the collection had grown a great deal. Thimbles became a favorite gift to receive on holidays and birthdays. Family members contributed thimbles with family backgrounds. A personal history added greatly to their value to the author.

A hint to the beginning collector, or anyone with a collection of any type, that the author has found to be very beneficial is to keep a file on the collection. The author uses three-by-five-inch index cards. As each new thimble is added, an index card is made out for it, containing the material of which it is made, any marks on it such as size and/or marker's mark, any known history of it, where it was obtained, the date it was obtained, and, if known, how much it cost. The card is then completed by a rough sketch of the thimble, showing its design. Matching, small, numbered, gummed stickers are placed on the thimble and on the card so the art work is not the only means of identification.

These cards are then filed according to category, such as fancy silver, children's, advertising, etc. The cards are very helpful in keeping the collection up to date as more information is gathered, and they also help keep the value of the collection easily ascertainable. This last point is interesting to keep track of as time passes and as each thimble rises in value as it becomes older.

As the collection grows, the collector becomes more and more "hooked" on thimbles. He finds he is doing research to discover more about thimbles and their place in the world's history. Many tangent interests develop. In the case of the author, this led to the writing of this book.

ANTIQUE AND UNUSUAL THIMBLES

THIMBLE PRICE GUIDE

A Under $5
B $5-$10
C $10-$15
D $15-$25
E $25-$35
F $35-$50
G $50-$75
H $75-$100
I $100-$200
J Over $200
K $300-$500
L $750-$10,000

1 DEFINITIONS

ACCORDING to *A Dictionary of Arts Manufacturers and Mines* by Andrew Ure, published in New York in 1865, a thimble is

> a small truncated metallic cone, deviating a little from a cylinder, smooth within, and symetrically pitted on the outside with numerous rows of indentations, which is put upon the tip of the middle finger of the right hand, to enable it to push the needle readily and safely through cloth or leather in the act of sewing. This little instrument is fashioned in two ways; either with a pitted end, or without one; the latter, called the open thimble, being employed by tailors, upholsterers, and generally speaking, by Needle-men.

That is, a thimble is an appliance fitted to the top of the middle finger of the right hand, used for the purpose of pressing the needle through any material to be sewn. It protects the fingers from the needle.

The English word came from the Anglo-Saxon *thymel* (related to the German *daumen,* meaning thumb). The word became corrupted into *thimmel, thimbil, thummie, thymel, thumbel,* and *themel.* A second theory is that the word is derived from the Scotch *thummel,* from "thumb-bell," a bell-shaped shield that was originally worn on the thumb. The French *dé* and Spanish *dedal* originated in the Latin *digitus,* meaning finger.

A close cousin of the thimble is the finger shield. It is probably a cousin to the early British *gwniadur* and is as old as the thimble itself. The earliest of these finger guards were made of horn, ivory, tortoiseshell, and other similar materials. These were sufficient for light sewing; but for heavier work they were made of metal. According to an old American dictionary of needlework it is

> a silver appliance made to fit the first finger of the left hand on which materials are laid and held by the thumb in plain sewing. It resembles a ring, one side being an inch wide, and the other quite as narrow as an ordinary finger ring. It is employed to protect the finger from the needle when much hard sewing has to be done or the finger has been accidentally hurt.

Such a shield is also used in Tambour embroidery. A tambour-work thimble was made from a piece of metal that was rolled round but was not joined. This style of construction was used so that the thimble could expand to the required size. It was worn on the forefinger of the right hand. The top of it was cut on a slope and had a notch at the highest point. This notch helped to guide the tambour hook. It also pressed down the fabric as the stitch was brought through to the upper surface. Since tambour embroidery is seldom done today, the tambour thimble is seldom seen.

Sometimes a modern finger shield made of celluloid or plastic can be found, but generally the finger shield is a part of needlework history.

Sterling finger guard, left hand. C. 1910. (D)

Sterling finger guard worn on finger under work to protect work from blood from pricked finger. (E)

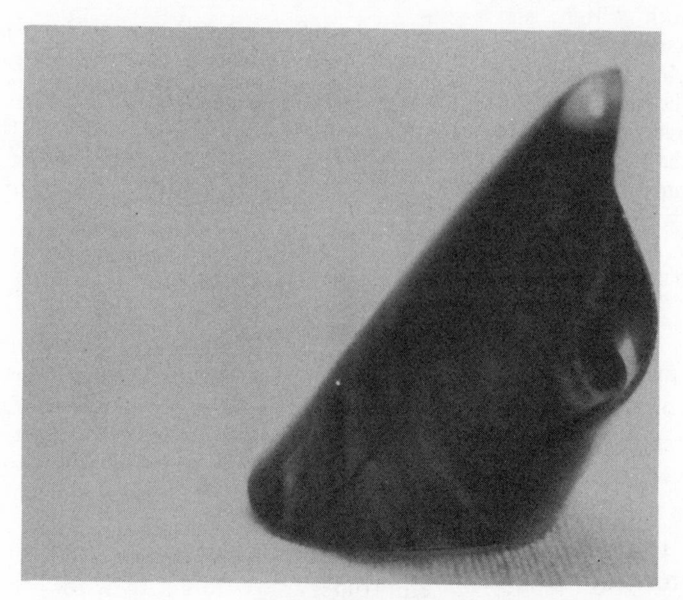

Finger shield, plastic. Looks like a tortoiseshell; wrap over back–modern. (A)

2 THIMBLE TALES

THIMBLES occasionally had uses other than in sewing. An interesting example was the "dames thimbles." These were heavy iron thimbles and were used by the dames of small children's schools. When correction of the children's behavior was considered necessary, this thimble was tapped sharply and vigorously on the pupil's head. This much-dreaded punishment was called "thimble-pie making."

Thimbles were also brought to mind by a children's game called "Thimble, Thimble, Who's Got the Thimble?" And most children can tell the forgetful adult about Thumbelina. She was the little maiden who was so very small that she could fit into a thimble, or thumbel, and whose dainty bed was made from a walnut shell that was most delicately carved and polished. Illustrations of this fairy tale usually show the thimble to be very delicate. It is often of china and ornamented with delicate flower sprays.

The thimble also appears in the tale of Peter Pan. Peter gave Wendy a kiss that was in the form of a thimble. Miss Maude Adams, an actress who played the part of Peter Pan, gave a miniature gold "kiss" to her friends.

In *McGuffey's Second Reader,* published in 1836, the following tale was used to show a point of morals to the reader:

A PLACE FOR EVERYTHING

MARY: I wish you would lend me your thimble. I can never find my own.

SARAH: Why is it, Mary, you can never find it. I have a place for everything and I put everything in its place when I have done using it.

MARY: I am ashamed. Before tonight I will have a place for everything. You have taught me a lesson.

The thimble also plays a part in Greek mythology. Venus was sewing on her cloaks in a Cyprian grove when she pricked her finger with her needle. She had her doves carry her in her coach to Jove. She showed him an "ivory finger stained with purple blood" and begged him to make her invulnerable. Jove was angry and told her to "go and stitch no more." But, in the manner of most women, Venus was upset about the possibility of having to appear at the feasts of the Goddesses dressed in rags or even naked; therefore, she appealed to Vulcan, who took pity on her. He told her that no needle would ever give her pain again and "in a shell of brass her finger cased."

One of literature's greatest, Shakespeare, mentions thimbles in two of his famous plays. In *King John* he wrote:

> Your ladies and pale visag'd maids,
> Like amazons, come tripping after
> drums;
> Their thimbles into armed guantlets
> change,
> Their needles into lances.

Another mention of thimbles is in the popular *Taming of the Shrew:*

> And that I'll prove upon thee
> Though thy little finger be armed
> in a Thimble.

One would not ordinarily associate thimbles with "ladies of the night," but it is said that these ladies tapped thimbles against the glass in their windows to get the attention of gentlemen passing by; hence, the street where they worked is called Thimble-Knocking Street.

Thimbles were also connected with the shady side of life during the years of Prohibition in the United States. A shot glass in the shape of a thimble usually had the motto Just a Thimble Full around the rim.

In 1866 a silver thimble, borrowed from Miss Emily Fitzgerald, daughter of the Knight of Kerry, played an important part in the progress of modern communications. This thimble, now in the possession of the Science Museum, South Kensington, England, with the addition of a few drops of acid and a wire of zinc formed the "battery" from which a current was passed through the first telegraph cables laid across the Atlantic Ocean. The two cables went from Valentia, Ireland, to Newfoundland. The building in which the cables terminated, known as Telegraph House, was built on land owned by Miss Fitzgerald's father.

Thimbles are also used in the field of music. Many country-music groups include a player who wears ten thimbles, one on each finger, and rubs them up and down the ribs of a metal washboard.

3 *THIMBLE* IN MANY LANGUAGES

IT is interesting to see the similarities and differences in the word *thimble* in different languages. Maybe this list will help the world traveler with her collection.

COUNTRY	WORD
Holland	*Vingerhoed*
Norway	*Fingerfort*
Italy	*Ditali*
Germany	*Fingerhut*
Mexico	*Dedales*
Portugal	*Dedales*
Spain	*Dedales*
Korea	*Kolmi*
Hungary	*Gyuszu*
France	*Dé*
Wales	*Gwyniadur* or *Gwniadur* or *Byswain*—Finger Shield
Japan	指 *yubi* finger 貫 *nu* to pull out き *ki* to draw out

4 ANATOMY OF A THIMBLE

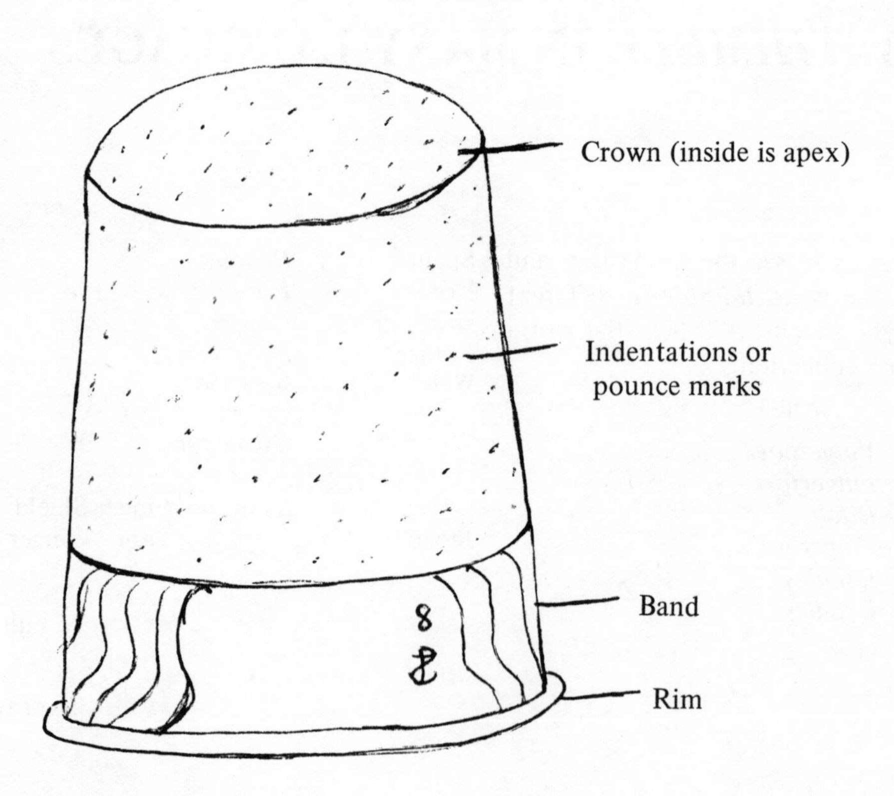

THE thimble is made up of three main parts: the top or crown; the sides, which have the indentations; and the band—and many have a rim at the bottom of the band. The inside of the thimble has the sides and the apex. The apex is the other side of the crown. When looking at a thimble, the collector should not neglect the apex, as many thimbles have marks there. The other main area to inspect for identification marks is the band. If there is a decoration around the band, it often does not fully encircle the band but, instead, leaves a blank space. This space was allowed so the thimble could be monogrammed with the initials or name of the owner if desired. The marks are often put at the side of this monogram space.

5 THIMBLE SIZES

By the middle of the nineteenth century, thimbles were marked with a size number.

Thimbles are made in many different sizes. They should fit comfortably on the end of the finger. If the thimble is too tight the finger will sweat, and if it is too large the thimble will fall off. The sizes used vary in different countries. This is a chart of approximate size comparisons according to country:

COUNTRY	SMALL	MEDIUM	LARGE
United States	6, 7, 8	9, 10, 11	12
British	9, 8, 7	6, 5	4, 3
French	8	9 10	11 12
German and Dutch	3, 4	5, 6, 7	8, 9, 10
Norwegian	1 2	3 4	

In the United States thimble size relates to ring size in this manner:

Ring Gauge	3	3½	4	4½	5	5½	6	7	7½	8	8½
Thimble size	6	7	8	9	10	11	12	13	14	15	16

6 MARKS

WHEN a thimble was made, one of the last things to be done was the application of whatever marks were necessary or desired. Some thimbles have marks, some do not. The place and the time of the thimble's manufacture are factors that determined what marks, if any, were used.

In England the guild system carefully controlled the manufacture of silver and gold objects–including thimbles. With their system, called hallmarking, they could guarantee the quality of the object to the purchaser because the object had to meet the rigid requirements of the guild in order to be marked; thus, any object with the hallmarks was of good quality. Included in the hallmarks are symbols that stand for the silversmith who made the object, the place of manufacture, and the year of manufacture.

It would seem that the thimble collector would have no trouble identifying English silver thimbles. Unfortunately there are problems. Thimbles are so small that the regulations of the Assay Offices were not always strictly enforced. When they were and the marks were put on the thimble, they were not always decipherable.

Another problem is that, from 1738 until 1792, gold and silver thimbles were given an exemption from hallmark regulations. In 1792 the exemption was withdrawn from thimbles of silver that weighed more than five pennyweight. Many silversmiths, however, knowing that the public was used to associating hallmarks with quality, requested that their thimbles have the hallmarks applied by the Assay Office. This option remains open to English silversmiths today.

One helpful fact in dating English silver thimbles is that until 1890 the monarch's head-duty stamp was included in the hallmark.

Sometimes, other European countries mark their thimbles, but a system like the English hallmark system is not used. Thimbles can be found with the name of the country of manufacture stamped on them. This applies to thimbles of silver as well as to thimbles of other materials. English thimbles, other than silver, can have "England" stamped on them.

In America no uniform marking system was used; in fact, many objects were not marked in any way. But since many American silversmiths had a British heritage, they were accustomed to using some sort of mark on their wares; therefore, many American thimbles have some kind of identification mark. Often it consists of the name or the initials of the silversmith. This touchmark was usually placed in a rectangle, oval, circle, shield, or other geometric shape. Some silversmiths used other devices such as a fleur-de-lis, a crown, a pellet, or a star with their mark. American thimbles have no date or place-of-manufacture mark.

Another problem in identifying American thimbles is that silversmiths did not use only one mark. Each one had a number of ways of marking his wares and used the assortment of marks at all times; therefore, a particular piece cannot be dated by which type of mark the silversmith used on it.

A general rule, which was not always followed, is that during the first quarter of the eighteenth century it was a common practice for the silversmith to use his surname—either with or without his initial. Sometimes he used his full name. Often, until 1770, only initials were used. The general use of a geometric device along with the maker's initial was not employed until the middle of the eighteenth century.

As the century progressed and the silver company took the place of the individual silversmith, the use of a company mark was adopted. Many thimbles are found with a company mark instead of the mark of a silversmith. Some of the most frequently found marks follow:

Marks of Early American Silversmiths Known to Have Made Thimbles

Halsted, Benjamin
New York, New York
worked 1764 - 1806

Halsted

HALSTED · NY

Pratt, Nathan
New York, New York
worked 1772 - 1842

N. PRATT

Lupp, Henry
New Brunswick, N. J.
worked 1783

H Lupp

Dodge, Nehemiah
Providence, R. I.
worked 1795 - 1824

N. DODGE

N. DODGE

Ketcham, James
New York, New York
worked 1807 - 1823

I KETCHAM

Platt & Brother
New York, New York
worked 1820

PLATT + BROTHER

PLATT + BRO

Peters, James
Philadelphia, Pa.
worked 1821 - 1850

J. PETERS

Webster, Henry L.
Providence, R. I.
worked 1831

H.L. WEBSTER

Hinsdale, Epaphras
New York, New York
worked 1797

HINSDALE

Gorham, Jabez
Providence, R. I.
worked 1842

J GORHAM

Marks of American Thimble Manufacturers

Simons Brothers Company — mark found in apex

Philadelphia, Pa.

Simons Industrial — mark found in apex

18% Nickel
60% Copper
22% Zinc

Ketcham & McDougall — mark found in apex

Brooklyn, N. Y.

Thomas F. Brogan — mark found in apex

New York, N. Y.

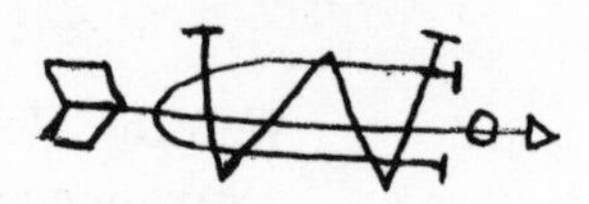

Webster Company — mark found in apex

N. Attelboro, Mass.

Waith Thresher Company — mark found in apex

Providence, R. I.

made by Waith Thresher for — mark found in apex

D. C. Percival of Boston, Mass.

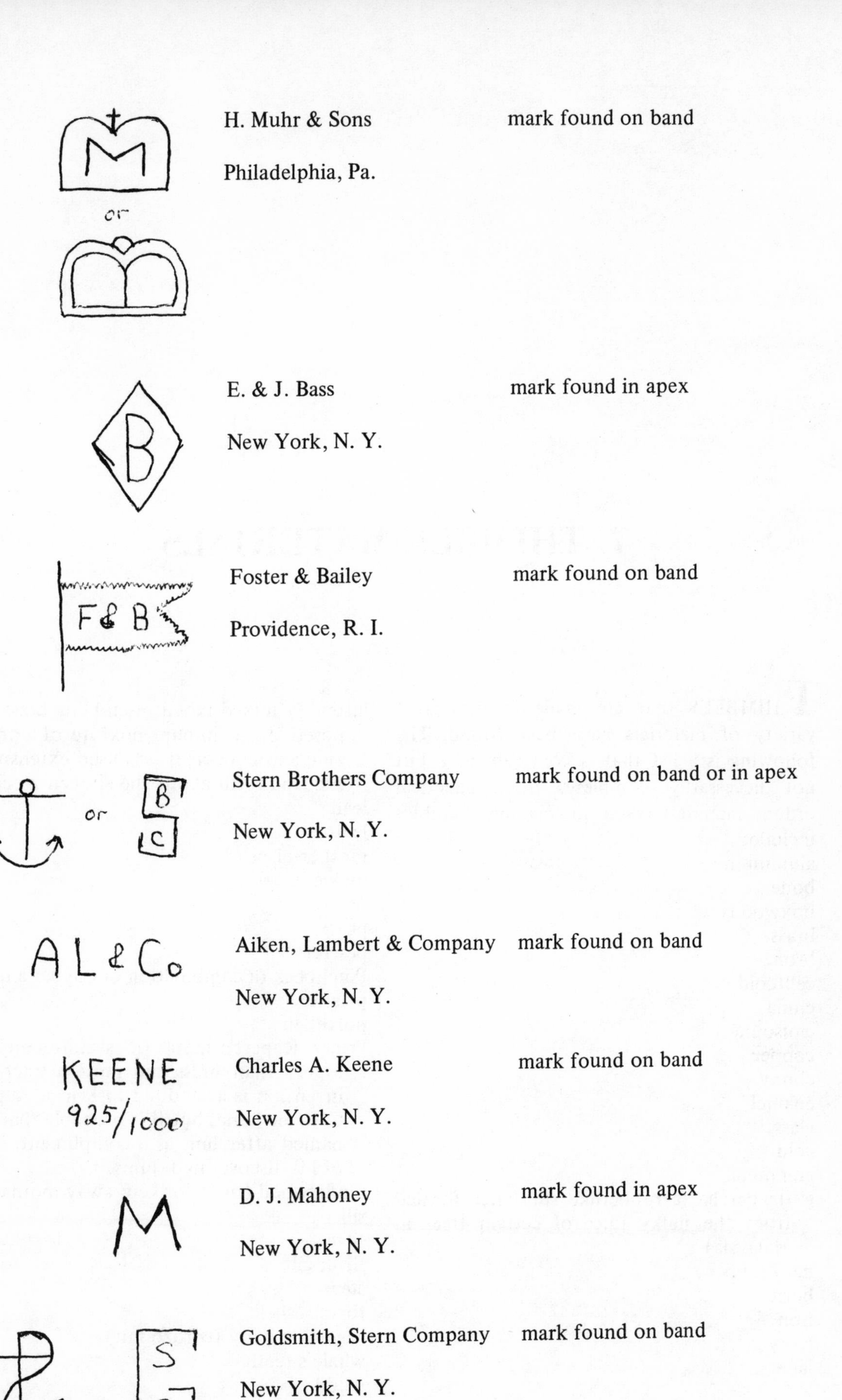

H. Muhr & Sons	Philadelphia, Pa.	mark found on band
E. & J. Bass	New York, N. Y.	mark found in apex
Foster & Bailey	Providence, R. I.	mark found on band
Stern Brothers Company	New York, N. Y.	mark found on band or in apex
Aiken, Lambert & Company	New York, N. Y.	mark found on band
Charles A. Keene	New York, N. Y.	mark found on band
D. J. Mahoney	New York, N. Y.	mark found in apex
Goldsmith, Stern Company	New York, N. Y.	mark found on band

7 THIMBLE MATERIALS

THIMBLES that are made from a great variety of materials have been found. The following is a list that is comprehensive but not necessarily complete. In alphabetical order, materials used in making thimbles include:

aluminum
bone
boxwood
brass
bronze
celluloid
china
cloisonné
copper
ebony
enamel
glass
gold
gun metal
gutta percha (a rubberlike substance formed from the milky juice of certain trees in Malaysia)
hard rubber
horn
iron
ivory
jade
latten (a mixed metal resembling brass, composed of an impure mixture of unrefined zinc and copper; it was used extensively in England until about the sixteenth century)
lead
leather
mother-of-pearl
nickle
onyx
pearl
pewter
Pinchbeck (a combination of copper and zinc)
plastic
porcelain
Prince Rupert's metal (it is more coppery in aspect than brass and more attractive; its invention is accredited to Prince Rupert of Cavalier fame, but it is probable that it was named after him as a compliment, instead of his discovering it himself)
sandalwood (the odor kept away moths)
silk
silver
silver-gilt
steel
tortoiseshell
vegetable ivory (corozo nut)
whale's teeth
wood

Sterling–Peru. Type of thimble used by Indians in Lima. Modern. (C)

Sterling–Mexico. Applied wirework. Modern. (B)

Sterling–Navajo Indian. Modern. (C)

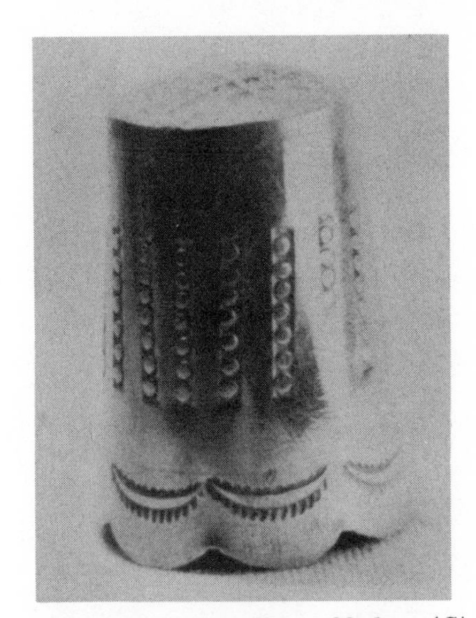

Silver–Mexico. Handmade. Modern. (C)

Sterling–Mexico. Applied wirework. Modern. (B)

Sterling–Mexico. Applied wirework; narrow abalone band. Modern. (B)

Gold-toned metal, Spain. "Toledo." Green, blue, red, white on border. Modern. (A)

Leather–Korea. Silk covered; red, gold, black, and green stitching. (A)

Metal–Greece. Modern. (A)

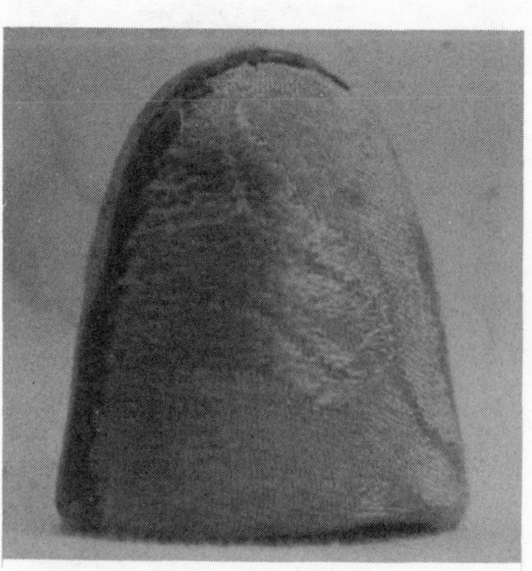

Leather. Asian. Covered with pink and green silk and blue stitching. (C)

Leather–Korea. Black and green with red stitching. (A)

Copper–Austria. Petit point band; roses and leaves on blue background. (B)

etal–India. Marked "KIWI" upside down. *(A)*

Sailor's Palm–leather and metal. Used by sailors to sew sails. Modern. (A)

Made by Corning Glass in 1918, for use by soldiers in World War I–part of sewing kit. (E)

Sterling–Germany. Stars on ribbed background. (C)

Shoemaker's. Leather and metal. Leather ring with square metal plate. (F)

Sterling–Germany. Stars band. (C)

Sterling–Germany. Dots and diamonds band. (C)

White metal. Snake and dot band. (B)

Nickel. Dotted scallop band. S.B.C. mark. (C)

Metal. Palmate band. (A)

Nickel. Leaf and berry band. SBC mark. (C)

Metal. Germany, double-ribbed band. (A)

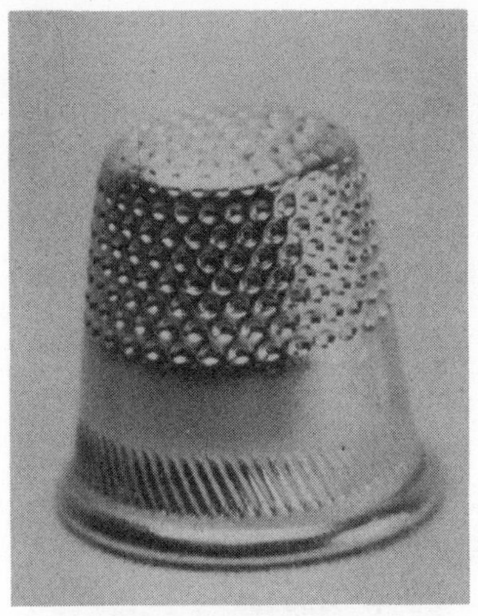

Gold-toned aluminum. Japan, diagonal-slashed band. (A)

Metal. Dotted band. (A)

Metal. Chrysanthemums band. (B)

Metal. Germany, double narrow-ribbed band. (A)

Metal. Top looks like silver ; bottom looks like brass. (A)

Cotton white crocheted. Scalloped border. (A)

Copper lined with steel. (B)

Metal–"Iles." (B)

8 HOW THIMBLES ARE MADE

THE thimble-making process has progressed through the years. The rate of progress differed in different parts of the world.

From remaining examples it seems that the Greek and Roman craftsmen were well acquainted with the process of die stamping and turning and spinning metal objects in a lathe. They also knew of casting by the waste-wax process. Thimbles made in that manner needed little further treatment.

An example from England, dating from the fifteenth century, indicates that the indentations were then being made there on a lathe. In this process, the thimble was fixed in a chuck that fit its internal diameter exactly. It was then revolved while a knurled wheel was pressed against it. A series of shallow grooves guided the revolving wheel.

Early thimbles of the classical era were of two varieties that still exist as similar forms in todays Western world. The first of these is the "ring" type. It was formed by a strip of metal that was simply rolled around to form a band or ring, usually about ¾ of an inch wide and soldered at the joint. The ends were left open, and the thimble was slipped over the top joint of the finger, leaving the tip unprotected. In certain types of sewing, especially sewing very heavy materials, it is the side of the finger, not the top, that is used for pushing the needle through the fabric; therefore, in work of this type, the covered end would be superfluous and even cumbersome.

The other type that the Western world is familiar with is known as the "sugarloaf" type. In it the tip of the finger is protected by the thimble, which has a covered top. In the Greek and Roman examples, the tops often had a defined conic shape. The whole thimble might only be one inch high. In later centuries, in Spain and elsewhere, the conical shape appeared again. It was larger and longer, sometimes as much as 2¾ inches high. It is possible that the pointed tip was used as an awl or punch to make holes for the needle to go through. This conical type has not been used in Europe for the last four or five centuries. Instead, the domed type we see today gained in public favor.

The pointed sugarloaf type seems to have been made in one piece. It was punched or moulded, depending on the type of metal used. The domed or rounded type that was more popular was usually made in two sections. In both types the apex frequently was left smooth, especially in the longer or taller types. Only the main body of the thimble was pounced. The plain band around the rim seems to have been a feature of most of these thimbles. If the pounce marks were made all the way down to the bottom of the thimble, there would have been a great probability that the needle would slip and injure the finger. But with the plain band at the bottom, the wearer was forced to use only the upper section of the thimble; therefore, in nearly all ages and in all countries, a plain finishing band is found on both ring and sugar-loaf types of thimbles.

The question of whether or not the pounce marks continued up and over the crown of the sugar-loaf thimble seems to have been left to the whim of the individual doing the pouncing. Since the top could not be used for pushing the needle, only the side was used. On the more rounded type of thimble the pounce marks could have been used so there was more of a chance that the top would have been used in sewing.

From some sixteenth-century examples it appears that the indentations were knurled in, but not in single rows. Instead, several knurled wheels were mounted together on the same tool. This particular method has been developed to great perfection in modern days. Inscriptions and decorations have been rolled on thimbles in the same manner.

In other sixteenth-century examples, a different method of manufacture was used. In this type the dome was cone-shaped. The rim was often engraved with a short motto or a line of verse. This is a custom that was repeated in the early part of the eighteenth century and again in Victorian days.

In the sixteenth century some thimbles were made in two sections. The domed upper third was hand-raised or cast, and it was covered with hand-punched indentations. The lower portion was shaped from a plate of metal and vertically seamed. The joints were practically invisible. In some, the tip was almost flat. This tip was inserted into a slightly tapering cylinder and then soldered in place. Many of these thimbles were squat in shape and were heavy. Sometimes they were reinforced with an inner lining made from one piece of brass. This type of construction seems to have been used into the seventeenth century.

Other than a single incised line, these early thimbles had no decoration around the open end of the thimble. The edge was not reinforced or rolled.

The indentations on these thimbles were applied in an uneven spiral beginning at the open end and continuing up to the crown. The indentations often ended before reaching the center of the crown, leaving a smooth tonsurelike area at the apex. A few of these thimbles have a stamped maker's mark preceding the first indentation at the start of the spiral.

By the middle of the seventeenth century, very tall thimbles were popular. They were made in two parts. The open end was rolled outward or sometimes a separate band about one millimeter wide was attached to the outside. The indentations on the sides were done in a wide strip, using a multitoothed tool. A spiral treatment of the crown was used with this method of manufacture.

At the beginning of the eighteenth century, the crowns of the thimbles were usually pattern-stamped. The indentations were made on a straight line. This gave the top a hatched appearance.

Starting in the seventeenth century, the thimble might have had a plain narrow rim that could have been engraved with the name of the owner. Patterned bands were stamped around the open end at this time. Some were turned to decorate them with grooves and bands.

In early Georgian days the band, if it was not plain, could have been flat-chased and engraved with scrolls or with a cartouche enclosing a tiny crest or cypher. Wreaths of flowers and foliage were also used as decoration.

During the late Georgian days, thimbles were made in a single piece by spinning. Some of these were banded above the rim with filigree work. This was made separately from flat wire and soldered on its edge to the background silver. The scrolled pattern could have included a shield-shaped or oval panel that was engraved with the owners crest. Some thimbles even had jewels around the rim.

In the early nineteenth century the same types of rim decorations were used. Some thimbles were engraved with the bright-cut technique.

In America, thimble-manufacturing methods evolved in a similar fashion as the years passed. Many of the seventeenth-century American thimbles had domed tops that the silversmith fashioned by hand using a concave die and convex tool. The small disk of metal was placed between these, and the convex part was struck with a hammer.

This top was then joined to the sides with silver solder. The indentations were made with a tool that had protrusions. The inside of the thimble was first fitted tightly to a mandrel, which prevented the indentations from creating uncomfortable projections on the inside. Sometimes only the top of the thimble was indented. These indentations were made by hand using a convex punch. This type of thimble had the sides free for an engraved decoration, such as flowers, initials, or the full name of the owner. Often the rim on these thimbles was of round or flatdrawn wire, which was soldered to the foot of the thimble.

In the eighteenth century some of the thimbles made in America were constructed from a single piece of silver. The silversmith punched out from a flat plate of the metal a disk of the proper diameter. This disk was then hammered into a series of increasingly concave holes in a tool called a thimble stamp. This method of manufacture was also used in the sixteenth and seventeenth centuries in Europe, as illustrated by contemporary engravings that show the silversmiths at work. In the 1700s a thimble stamp was usually included in lists of silversmith's tools.

Until the invention in the middle of the eighteenth century of the "nose machine," thimble indentations were hand punched; therefore they show irregular spacing. After this time they were impressed in a symmetrical manner.

Early in the nineteenth century, patents were granted for machines that mechanically made thimbles and that also rimmed them without solder. All the decoration, however, continued to be done by hand. This included punchwork, flat chasing, engraving, bright cut, and other similar methods. But by the second quarter of the century, simple repeat designs were being impressed by rollers while the thimble was on the lathe.

Therefore, by 1840 and the advent of the stamping machines, thimbles were being produced so quickly by these machines that there seemed to be no point in doing the hard work of hand manufacture. The mechanization was so complete that by 1870 the hand-crafted thimble was a thing of the past. Thimbles were made by machines in factories. One way of telling the age of a thimble is by the decoration. If it were made prior to the mid-nineteenth century, then the hand-done decoration will not be perfectly symmetrical.

9 THIMBLES AND ARCHAEOLOGY

NUMEROUS thimbles have been found in archaeological digs in both Europe and America. These thimbles show the history of thimbles in relation to their place in everyday life and also allow for the study of design evolution in the thimble.

About the oldest found are of bronze and of the open-ended style. These were found in the ruins of Pompeii and Herculaneum. Both these places were buried by the eruption of Mt. Vesuvius in A.D. 79. This proves that thimbles were in use that early in world history.

The *Journal of the British Archaeological Association* of 1879 contains an article, "On Thimbles," by H. Syer Cuming. In it a thimble is described in the following manner:

> (It) has the lower band stamped with a little shield charged with a cinquefoil, the form of which will hardly permit us to assign the thimble to a later epoch than c 1500. This specimen is of stout brass, ten-twelfths of an inch high; the top domed and with the sides thickly covered with a spiral of large indentations.

A second thimble, from the sixteenth century, is also mentioned. The top and most of the sides are indented. The lower sides are encircled by a band of sixteen circlets with an eleven-rayed star in each. A third is similar but has the words "God Save the Queen" around it instead of the belt of stars. That saying was fashionable in Elizabethan days.

The same article also mentions an ancient thimble dug out of the ruins of Stocks Market, with the motto "I wis it Better," which would seem to be of the same period.

Yet another thimble in the article by Mr. Cuming is of Prince Rupert's metal. "The slightly domed top is smooth, with a ring round its margin; the upper part of the sides is indented, the lower decorated with a scroll pattern, and there is a trifling rim at the base. This thimble is really a tasteful little thing in its way."

During the excavation of London Wall a number of thimbles were found made of latten and which dated from between the early sixteenth century and the latter part of the seventeenth.

When a house in England that dates back to the 1200s had an old wooden window sill renewed, a gold thimble was found. The thimble must have fallen into a crack between the wood and the masonry, and must have remained hidden there a considerable period of time, since no member of the family that owns the house could remember having seen it or hearing any mention of it. This charming thimble was worn and dented when found. It was so dark that it looked like common metal, but polishing revealed a lovely golden shine. It seems to date from the late seventeenth or early eighteenth century. There are traces of beveling around the rim. It bears the inscription "The Absent Ever Dear," combined with oak leaves in a band above the rim.

The *Illustrated London News* of 23 August 1958 reports the discovery of four engraved caps of bronze at the site of a medieval church on the west coast of Mainland, Shetland Isles. It is thought that three of the "thimbles" may have been shield ornaments, and the fourth a sword pommel-cap.

Archaeology has also played an important part in the study of American thimbles. Brass thimbles are among the most common small domestic objects found on Colonial and later sites. Various digs have shown that the thimbles varied in size, thickness, and the coarseness of the indentations, depending upon the intended materials to be sewn. There was a gradual change in styles, but we have no guarantee that all thimbles kept in step with the evolution.

Buried treasure in the form of old silver was found when Colonel H. Anthony Dyer built a house around the old chimney on the Willitt site. This was a decaying landmark east of Riverside, Rhode Island. During the excavations a workman unearthed a bent and flattened bit of silver that, when straightened out, proved to be an old-fashioned topless thimble in virtually perfect condition. It has, besides the usual little square or circular indentations, two roughly executed designs: one a flower that could be either a daisy or a sunflower; the other, a heart. Below these designs is the inscription "Ester Willitt." This is important because it is known that this was the name of one of the former occupants of the old house. Ester was born in 1648 and was married to Josiah Flint of Dorchester in 1672, so the thimble probably dates from before 1672. She probably used the thimble between 1660 and 1665.

It is possible that Robert Sanderson and John Hull of Boston made the thimble, as they did other work for the Willitt family. The heart and flower they used as decorations were typical of American motifs of that period. The thimble is of the topless variety and tapers slightly. The cylinder was shaped from a flat piece of silver and vertically seamed, as most sixteenth-century English thimbles were made. It has no maker's marks or hallmarks.

Two other thimbles dug up in America appear to have an interesting history. These seventeenth-century silver thimbles were found buried with Princess Ninigret (otherwise known as Weunquesh, chief sachem of the Narragansett Indians). She succeeded her father in 1676 and reigned until her death in about the year 1690.

One of the thimbles is topped and is similar in style to the thimbles of today. The other is topless. It is made of a sheet of silver bent into a cone. The fact that it was originally soldered together is shown by the design. It was cut after the seam was closed. Unfortunately, the solder was not strong enough and the seam has opened. It has neither hallmarks nor maker's marks.

The Princess may have received the thimbles in trade. In the nineteenth century, thimbles were used to trade with the Plains Indians. Many have been found on Indian sites that have small holes punched in the crown. This enabled them to be hung over a bead on thongs and used as "tinklers" to ornament their clothing and pouches.

Numerous thimbles have been recovered from sites in Williamsburg, Virginia, while the restorations were being done. Six brass ones were found on the Anthony Hay Site during the 1959-1960 excavations there. They all date from the period 1760 to 1790. They have indentations that are round, oval, pear-shaped, and square.

Reading of these examples makes the collector dream of digging up the backyard and finding "thimble" treasure.

10 HISTORY IN EUROPE

IT is generally believed that some kind of "needle pusher" has been used since man first started to sew. The first thimble was probably an unsophisticated device such as a piece of stone, wood, or bone of convenient shape, square with grooves and indentations, that was tied to the finger. A Stone Age woman might have used such a tool when the needle was first invented. An Egyptian example has been found. As fashion developed and required special techniques to be used for its adornments, more specialized tools were developed to meet these needs. Evidence of a thimble-type tool has been authenticated to 300 B.C. in Syria.

The next advance was a small, bell-shaped leather cap that was worn on the thumb. A strong piece of leather was stitched up one side, with a leather cap sewn across the top. This offered a primitive sort of protection while sewing. The word *thimble* is derived from the Old English *thymel,* meaning thumb stall.

Following the leather, in civilized countries, a metal thimble was developed at a very early time. Under difficult, primitive circumstances, much creative skill was used to produce this small but necessary object. The early Romans made a metal thimble that was quite similar to the kind we use today. In England a thimble such as this was known before the Dark Ages. Two words in the old British tongue seem to indicate that the early thimbles were made of a material selected for protection, such as bronze or iron, instead of a finer metal to be used as an adornment. The Welsh word *gwyniadur* or *gwniadur,* still used today, literally means "sewing-steel." Another word, *byswain,* means "finger-guard" or "shield." This makes it seem probable that the ancient Britons had actually looked for a form of armor for their finger as they sewed their skin garments or the tough hides that they used for bed coverings and door curtains. By classical times, Britain was well known to both the Greeks and the Romans for beautiful woolen, multi-colored, plaidlike garments. These were skillfully made and thus disprove the stereotype of savages wearing animal skins.

These early metal thimbles were usually one of two types: a heavy metal that was cast and had irregularly placed indentations; or a finer type made from a sheet of metal, which had neatly arranged indentations.

The open-top design that some of these

early thimbles had was useful because it enabled the sensitive fingertip to be exposed. A typical example is a cast-bronze ring that is ¼ inch wide and has three rows of indentations arranged in a diamond-type design. It was probably cast in a stone mold and was trimmed after being cast. The indentations were then added by hand. This type of thimble was worn as comfortably as a finger ring.

A Medieval thimble that was uncovered at Weoley Castle, near Birmingham, has been dated at A.D. 1400-1550. It has the more modern design of a rounded top and a slender body. Other Medieval thimbles have been found that date from A.D. 1200 until the end of the fifteenth century. Most are from the A.D. 1400 period. They show the difference between the "sugar-loaf" type of earlier days and the "domed" or rounded top.

On the Continent, bone thimbles are known to have been made during, and probably after, the Roman occupation. In England, however, no early bone thimbles were found. From the beginning of the Dark Ages until the twelfth or thirteenth centuries in England, the *themel* or leather thimble appears to have been used. Different races can use the same tools differently or use a completely different tool. The Scandinavians, who are noted for their embroidery and needlework, brought their own type of tools to England when they invaded the British Isles. They used the *thummel* instead of the Roman type of thimble; therefore, it can be deduced that they pulled the needle through the fabric instead of pushing it through. Pushing would have required a thimble of the ring or sugar-loaf type.

At first the thummel was worn on the thumb where it was practical for working on flat, fairly soft surfaces that were held in the hand. It gradually came to be worn on the finger—probably during the 1250-1350 period. This was the famous *opus Anglicanum,* or gold-work period; however, the name remained as a reminder of the original way of use. The Continental names for the thimble retain the Roman origin, but in England the Scandinavian invaders brought their own language and style of thimble. Eventually, the English returned to the metal thimble to protect the finger while doing needlework.

English women were famous for their excellent embroidery as early as A.D. 900. Records dating back to the seventh century mention the skill of the English embroideresses. It was at this time that Saint Etheldreda fashioned "with her own hands" the famous stole and maniple for Saint Cuthbert. It is richly embellished with gold and precious stones, and today is one of the treasures of Durham Cathedral.

Anglo-Saxon women used their talents in embroidery, making ecclesiastical vestments and furnishings. Unfortunately, few traces of metal thimbles from this period have been found. Perhaps the reason for this lies in the gold work itself. Inflexible metal thimbles would not have been of much use because the work was done at a frame on a heavy-backing material. This was especially needed for the large frontals, heavy banners, and other big pieces of work that the women executed. The size was a hindrance, often causing the work to slip and be cumbersome, even causing the fingers of the worker to be cut and bleed. They had to be attended to with bandages, and it is probable that these bandaged fingers brought about the idea of the leather thimble. It left the fingers sensitive and supple but, at the same time, provided protection against the steel needle. In this work, the side of the finger was used, instead of the tip, for pulling the needle through the stiff backing held taut on the frame. The leather thimble was the best tool to fit the situation.

When the *opus Anglicanum,* or "the English work," lost its popularity at about the time of the Black Death, the metal thimble came back into use. On the Continent the leather type was never used as much as in England because little gold work was done there.

Les Accessories du Coutume et du Mobilier by H.R. D'Allemagne gives much of the history of thimbles in France. By the thirteenth century, at least two companies in France were manufacturing thimbles. Thimbles of latten or brass were made by the *fermailleurs* or clasp and buckle makers. The *boutonniers,* or button-makers, manufactured thimbles of iron or copper. Workmen who made thimbles as well as clasps or buttons were known as *deéliers* or *déiliers.*

French thimbles began to have lavish decorations by the fourteenth century. This was much earlier than similar advances in other countries. Often they had owner's crests or coat-of-arms on them. Sprays of foliage and other ornamental motifs in relief were sometimes used instead of the normal indentations. A silver or gold band could be engraved with an inscription or a motto.

Thimble makers on the Continent were ahead of English thimble makers at this time because English thimbles were very plain and simple. The themmel was also still in use at that time.

A cup, shaped like a thimble and thought to be a typical example of the thimbles in common use at that time, was made for the Tailor's Guild of Nuremberg, Germany, in 1586. This five-inch-high cup shows the advances in manufacturing methods. It is made of brass that was plated with silver. The indentations appear to be knurled in, and it seems probable that several knurling wheels were mounted together. This method was further perfected and is in common use to this day.

The Nuremberg cup also shows that inscriptions and other parts of the thimble's decoration were rolled on by using the same method. The pattern was cut intaglio on a narrow roller, which was then pressed into the thimble as it revolved on the chuck. Around the edge is written *Vivat Die Ehrsame Schneiderzunft,* which means "Long Life to the Highly Esteemed Guild of Tailors."

The base of the cup was made separately and then soldered to the body, which was made from a sheet of metal that was bent into a tube shape and closed with a soldered seam. Tin was commonly used for the soldering. In many thimbles of this period the tin has perished and therefore the joint has opened and the method of manufacture is easily seen. Although some Medieval brass thimbles have been found that were made in one piece, by the Middle Ages thimbles were usually made in two pieces in that manner.

In Britain, as examples in the London Museum show, the two-piece method of manufacture was not adopted until the fifteenth or sixteenth century. It seems the later the date of manufacture, the more likely it is that the thimble was made in two pieces. We cannot be sure of the reason for this change in the method of manufacture. It was probably more simple to make a neat ring type and then add the flattish dome to it. Another possibility for the change is the fact that by using this method, a smaller and neater thimble could be made. This was not the only reason, however, since some very small thimbles have been made in one piece. It seems that the thinner the metal became, the greater the chances were that it was constructed in two pieces.

In the Kunstgewerbemuseum in Berlin are some Medieval thimbles from Germany. There is a small acorn-shaped one of bronze that has small indentations, and another made of gold-plated silver. It has a flat top that shows two heads painted under glass and dates from circa 1580-1600. This type was apparently popular in Germany at this period of time. Another one, also of gold-plated silver, has a similar flat top, but it has a floral design that is covered with a transparent material, which might be horn. On its side is the date 1606 with the letters *V G M N* above. The sides are decorated with a scroll ornament, and *Iunkfrau Ivstine von Herten* is engraved on the lower edge.

An earlier German thimble is of copper with a scroll ornament and has, engraved around the rim (translated), "Happiness and love no thief can steal from me." It is dated 1599.

A later thimble decorated with tendrils of leaves is datable from the four stamps on the inside. They are three crowns (Sweden), a crowned *G* (Goleborg), *I D B* (Johann Daniel Blomsterwall, Master, 1810-1841), and the karat marking (18K). These thimbles are from the A. Figdor of Vienna collection.

During the 1600s it seems that silver thimbles were frequently used by the middle classes in most of Europe; however, they were considered possessions of enough value that they were often listed in wills and other legal and important records. A French inventory dated 1693 lists among the effects of a person named Claudine Bouzonnet Stella "three silver thimbles." In England, besides on the Continent, the thimble had by this time begun its development from a utilitarian device into a possession that was worthy of being a special gift or momento.

During England's Civil War (from 1642 until 1652), the great Cavalier families contributed freely to the funds of King Charles II Royalists by giving up their silverware and gold plate. Parliamentary forces, even more so in the later years, were often given the name the "thimble and bodkin army" because of the number of these items given by their supporters. Political gifts of this kind are a recurring theme in English literature of the seventeenth century. Pepys, on 3 April 1663, mentions them in his *Diary*, saying that Hugh Peter's preaching during the Civil War stirred up the maids of the city to bring their bodkins and thimbles. Howell (1594-1669) in his *Philanglus* states that "the seamstress brought in her silver thimble, the chambermaid her bodkin and the cook her silver spoon." Popular ballads of the time refer to the sacrifice this way:

> And now for a fling at your thimbles,
> Your bodkins, rings and whistles,
> In truck for your toys
> We'll fit you with boys
> 'Tis the doctrine of Hugh's Epistles!

Another ballad said:

> To pull down their King
> Their plate they would bring
> And other precious things;
> So that Sedgwick and Peters
> Were no small getters
> By their bodkins, thimbles and rings.

Thimbles were also given for reasons other than political. In 1663, James Dillon, the future Lord Roscommon, after a visit to the Verneys at Claydon, sent a gift of two thimbles to Mary Verney and her cousin Doll Leake with an accompanying note so that "the one should not hurt a fine finger by the making of handkerchiefs, nor the other receive a prick in working my lady's buttons."

During these preindustrial-revolution times a large amount of domestic sewing was necessary in every household. Thimbles wore out quickly, and many people were dependent on the infrequent visits of peddlers for all objects of this kind; therefore, to young girls, a thimble of any metal would have been a very acceptable present.

In October 1763, Parson Woodforde wrote in his diary that he gave his sister Jenny a present of needles, pins, and two steel thimbles that he had bought in Oxford.

Some thimbles were designed to be given as gifts. Phrases around the rim of these thimbles acted as reminders: "A token of my esteem"; "Forget me not"; *Gage de mon amitié; Bin ich deine* (I am yours). A gift of an expensive piece of jewelry was often not permissible, but a gentleman could always properly give a lady a thimble or a thimble case as a token of his esteem. This gift was frequently used, and when used the giver would be remembered as the lady sewed.

Silver was not the only material from which thimbles were made during this period. Steel thimbles were sometimes lined with brass to add strength. Conversely, a thin brass thimble might have a steel band with indentations to take the full pressure of the needle around it.

Today we know toys as the playthings of children. During the seventeenth century, small household items, including sewing implements, were known as toys. Listed among the many items stocked by the toy seller dwelling "at the Green Parrot near Chancery Lane" in 1762 were "steel tops and other thimbles." This type of thimble was generally used by the ordinary woman.

Ladies of quality of the eighteenth century used a more delicate type of finger protection as they sewed. Gold was used quite a bit, as well as other unlikely materials. Thimbles of glass came from Venice and Bohemia. Thimbles of porcelain and china were manufactured by the great pottery firms in England and the Continent. Wooden thimbles were made in Germany and Austria.

In the latter part of the eighteenth century a particular feature of some gold and silver thimbles was *quatre-couleur* (four-color) work. It was often found in the decoration around the lower part of the thimble. It was usually in the form of grapes and vine, fruit, flowers, or oak leaves and acorns.

During the Regency period, much high-relief work was done. The great silversmiths of this period have left behind a number of examples, including the popular inlaid style.

The Regency period was also the time of the most beautiful porcelain thimbles. Some of these delicate thimbles had steel-lined tops, and occasionally the lower portion had an added strengthening band of steel, silver, or gold. Most of them, however, were simply made of china or porcelain. They usually had smooth sides with a painted scene or painted flowers, fruit, or birds. Except for the examples already mentioned, the tops usually were of china and had wide, bold ponce marks. A Meissen thimble of this era was a half-inch high and lined with gold. It was sold at auction at Christie's in London for £1,050. This rare thimble is decorated with amazing detail showing a harbor scene that features thirty figures, six bales of cotton, a large barrel, and a view of ships in the distance.

In France during the eighteenth century, thimbles became items of beauty just as they did in England. A large number of thimbles were set with precious stones. Others were decorated with motifs chased and engraved in different-colored golds. Besides precious metals, mother-of-pearl and tortoiseshell were used to make thimbles.

During the 1700s, France was plagued by internal revolution and external wars. This meant that by the beginning of the nineteenth century, precious metals were prohibitively expensive and difficult to obtain. Gold was beyond the reach of most people. Besides the problem of price, it was considered unpatriotic during the war to display lavish ornaments; therefore, French jewelers had to fashion necessary objects, including thimbles, out of steel and even iron. Their skill was so great that, according to D'Allemagne, "the beauty of the work was ample compensation for the small value of the material employed." Sieur Dumeny of Saint Julien-der-Sault was particularly well known for this type of work, his name often being found in lists and catalogues. A fine steel thimble of this period is difficult to obtain and is of great value. Steel thimbles by the firm of Rouy et Berthier were shown at the 1819 exhibition held in the Palais du Louvre. The judge's report says that these thimbles are "perfectly executed and of a pleasing shape, beautifully finished, and without any of the faults of thimbles in copper, gold, ivory, mother-of-pearl, and wood."

During this same exhibition a jeweler named Michaud Laboute showed thimbles "of which the interior was lined with platinum whilst the exterior was of silver." This was the first reliably dated reference to the practice of lining thimbles. As already stated, some china thimbles have a metal lining, but it has been disputed whether this was added later or incorporated when the thimbles were manufactured. In England during Victorian times and in the early part of this century, it was a usual practice to take silver thimbles that had worn thin and had prick marks in them to a jeweler who would run a small amount of silver around the interior—this, when set and burnished, formed a lining and made the thimble almost as good as new. This common service cost only a small amount of money; therefore, it seems probable that the idea of lining china thimbles came from the earlier practice of relining worn thimbles.

At the 1823 Exhibition of French Industrial Products the *verges-de-fer* thimbles were on view. These were similar to the great iron thimbles that were known in England as "Dame's thimmels." The schoolmistress rapped the heads of inattentive pupils with them. Both the *verge-de-fer* and "Dame's thimmels" might be called cousins to the type of thimble that was later known as the "Dorcas thimbles." It usually had an iron lining that made it durable and able to withstand heavy usage.

At that exhibit, thimbles of *doublé d'argent* and others of *doublé d'or* (silver and gold plate) were shown.

In the mid-nineteenth century in England, because of a popular book published at that time, a misconception about the origins of the thimble was believed. This was the theory that the thimble was invented at the end of the seventeenth century. Haydn's *Dictionary of Dates* was published in 1855 and was held as the educational standard in Victorian homes. It stated:

> THIMBLES This is of Dutch invention. The art of making them was brought to England by John Lofting, a mechanic from Holland, who set up a workshop at Islington, near London, and practiced the manufacture of them in various metals, with profit and sucess, about 1695.

In view of the archaeological evidence of thimbles from a much earlier date than this, and their mention in older literature and old inventories, it is evident that the author was mistaken; or it is possible that he intended to say that John Lofting had invented a new process for making thimbles—this seems likely. It was an improvement over the old methods and brought Lofting "profit and success."

In 1876 the *Dictionary of Dates* was revised by Benjamin Vincent. The error was corrected in this manner:

> THIMBLES are said to have been found at Herculaneum. The art of making them was brought to England by John Lofting . . . .

But, unfortunately, by that time the idea that thimbles were a fairly recent invention was firmly believed; therefore, no efforts were made to discover the early stages of its development.

It is now believed that what was actually brought to England was the art of sand casting. This was a recent development on the Continent. Since there was a supply of the right kind of sand there, he opened a workshop at Islington and manufactured cast thimbles in large numbers. Whether this method of manufacture was actually superior is debatable because when the thimbles were removed from the casting mold, they were in a very rough state. A considerable amount of work was required before they were comparable to the older type of thimble.

In an account of his journeys in the beginning of the eighteenth century, Daniel Defoe mentions two water mills at Great Marlow—"one for making of thimbles, a work excellently well finished and which performed to admiration."

In the time of Queen Victoria, thimbles came into their own. The industry and enthusiasm of the times carried over to needlework. There were quantities of thimbles produced but not always with the quality and elegance of the older ones. Especially numerous were silver thimbles because silver at the time was easily obtainable. Hundreds of different things were made of silver during this period. Almost every workbasket in the land had one silver thimble, if not more.

The Victorian love of gimmickry carried over to their thimbles. There were many "novelties." One Victorian example was shaped just like a finger with a clearly defined fingernail.

Victorian thimbles were made in large quantities at Birmingham and other industrial centers. Often there is only a small difference between the designs used, so there is little variety in Victorian thimbles. That may be the reason why the "gimmick" was so popular.

The Victorian workbasket usually held, besides a thimble or two, needles, emeries to keep them sharp, needlecases to keep them together, scissors, spool racks, sewing birds to help hold the work in place, tambour hooks, netting and tatting shuttles, and numerous other sewing implements.

After about 1850 thimbles generally became undistinguished and did not show great workmanship.

Today, there is no longer a factory that makes only thimbles. In 1963, Gabler Bros. of Schondorf, Germany, closed after 140 years of making thimbles.

11 HISTORY IN AMERICA

WHEN the first settlers came to the shores of America, they had to bring with them everything they needed to live, as there was nothing here but forests and Indians whom they considered savages; hence, the first thimbles, as well as all other sewing goods, were imported from Europe. In fact, the first commercial venture in America was in 1603 and included sewing tools. A group of merchants in England financed a ship full of goods for trading with the natives. It carried needles, thread, thimbles, and scissors to exchange for sassafras, which was in demand for the curative powers it contained. This ship sailed to the coast of the present state of Maine and went south as far as the future Plymouth Harbor.

The next references to thimbles in America are found in the newspapers of the colonies in the middle of the 1700s. The first such mention is an advertisement in *The Weekly Post Boy* of New York on 19 May 1746 that Thomas Brown, Cutler, at the Sign of the Cross Daggers near the Fly Market, "Sells all sorts of Ironmongery and cutlery Ware . . . Thimbles, Pins, and Needles."

The *Virginia Gazette,* in October 1751, had an early advertisement mentioning thimbles; they were offered for sale at the store near the church in Williamsburg.

In 1766 the *New York Weekly Post* advertised thimbles and scissors made by Thomas Brown, cutler; the *New York Gazette or Weekly Post-Boy* of 25 September 1766 advertised "a few best steel top thimbles" made by Benjamin Halstead.

The *New York Journal or The General Advertiser* of 6 August 1767 states: "Charles Shipman . . . lately from England (offers) ponce boxes and ivory thimbles, ivory netting and knotting needles." The *Boston News-Letter* of 22 October 1767 carried an advertisement that Daniel Boyer had imported steel top thimbles, as well as stamps for making them, from London.

The 27 October 1768 issue of the *Virginia Gazette* printed that Sarah Pitt of Williamsburg had recently imported "neat scissors in sheaths, superfine shaded crewels in grain, silver thimbles, morocco etwees with instruments complete, have plated or silver locks." The *Virginia Gazette* claimed that Mary Hill of Richmond had imported some silver thimbles from London and "will sell at a low advance for Money, Merchant Notes or Tobacco," in its 13 October 1771 issue.

It is only natural that as more advanced goods began to be made in America, thimbles came to be made here instead of being imported from Europe. Most were produced in the four principal centers of colonial silversmithing: Boston, Newport, New York, and Philadelphia. The *Charleston* (South Carolina) *City Gazette and Daily Advertiser* on 3 February 1798 carried an advertisement that stated that Edward Blackford and Company sold enameled and figured silver thimbles "imported" from New York.

It appears that the first thimbles made in any quantity in America were not of silver but of ivory. Charles Shipman, Ivory and Hardwood Turner, from Birmingham, England, advertised "ivory thimbles" and "eggs" among a long list of turner's articles in the *New York Journal for the General Advertiser* on 6 August 1767.

The first thimble factory in America was in Elizabeth Town, New Jersey. It was run by a silversmith named Benjamin Halsted. He was born in Elizabeth in 1734 and was apprenticed to a silversmith in New York. Admitted as a freeman silversmith in New York City, he first worked in New York from 1764 to 1766. Mr. Halsted must have been an interesting character, as evidenced by the August 1764 advertisement in the *New York Gazette*, run by Andrew Browne, warning the public to beware of Benjamin Halsted, who was apprenticed to him, as a dangerous character who "had bitten him for no reason."

In 1765 Halsted married and then worked in Elizabeth, starting in 1766. He was associated with his brother Matthias as a partner, and this new firm advertised the opening of its shop in *The New York Gazette or Weekly Post-Boy* on 18 September 1766.

> BENJAMIN AND MATTHIAS HALSTED, GOLD AND SILVERSMITHS
>
> Take this method to acquaint the public, that they have now set up, their business in Elizabeth-Town (nearly opposite to Mr. Joseph Jelf's merchant) where they propose to carry it on in all its branches, as the said Benjamin Halsted, has followed the business sometime in New-York, to the satisfaction of his employers, he hopes his former customers there and in the country will not forget him, as he will now obey all orders for work from them and other gentlemen and ladies of the city or country, at the shortest notice and most reasonable prices, with the greatest care and exactness to their entire satisfaction; as we propose to make work of all qualities (prices accordingly) we hope our employers will not expect the best of work for the meanest prices.
>
> Any orders for work being left at Mr. Thomas Star Tredwell's at Burling's-slip, New York, will come safe to hand; or any gentlemen or ladies wanting work done, that are desirous to see one of us to deliver their orders to, if they will please to leave word at the above Mr. Tredwell's, one or the other will wait on them at a very short notice.
>
> Said Matthias Halsted has for sale, a few silversmith's tools, which he will sell cheap, for cash, viz. Forging, planishing, hollowing and bouge hammers, piercing, riffling and common files, fine Turkey oil stone slips, and Bohemia polishing stones, double aqua fortis, corn, half corn and flour emery, borax, and sandever. The above tools & c. may be had of the above Mr. Tredwell, and likewise a few best steel top thimbles.
>
> Elizabeth-Town, September 17, 1766.

It is not known how long Benjamin Halsted worked in Elizabeth Town, but he worked in Philadelphia from 1783 to 1785 and again in New York from 1786 to 1806.

The *Diary or Evening Register* of 10 August 1794 printed this notice:

> BENJAMIN HALSTED–THIMBLE MANUFACTURY. Benjamin Halsted respectfully informs his Friends and the Public in general, that he still continues carrying on the gold and silversmith business No. 67 Broad Street; he has brought the manufactury of gold, silver, and Pinchbeck Thimbles with steel top to great perfection and thinks he could make a sufficient quantity to supply the United States Citizens, consider your interest, and encourage American Manufautures.
>
> Those imported are of the Slightest kind, I will engage that one of mine, will do more service than 3 of them, and I know by experience, that imported ones of the quality of mine cost 18 shillings per doz. and could not be sold by 25 percent, as low as mine. Every dealer in this article will soon find the advantage of keeping Halsted's Thimbles and have the satisfaction of knowing that he does his customers justice. Silver and steel Bodkins, tooth and ear picks by the doz. or single.

Benjamin Halsted's second son had his own thimble factory on Varick street, a few years before his father's death. Halsted's mark is the name "Halsted" in script in a conforming rectangle. One thimble that Halsted made has his mark on the inner rim. It is a family heirloom that has been passed down to each generation for well over one hundred years.

Unfortunately, many of the early thimbles made in America do not have marks on them. Jacob Hurd made his mark on a gold thimble that he made for Elizabeth Gooch between 1740 and 1750. From surviving records it is known that Myer Myers of New York, in 1755, filled an order for "11 Thimbles Silver," for which he charged £1/6/51, for a merchant from Philadelphia. It is also known that Paul Revere made a gold thimble for his wife, and his son continued to make "ladies' thimbles" after the death of his father.

One of the principal silversmiths of the early republic was Henry Lupp, who lived from 1760 to 1800 and practiced his trade from 1783 to 1800. He lived and worked in New Brunswick, New Jersey. This was an area of prosperous English, Dutch, and German families, and there was a demand for improved household equipment, including sewing items. An advertisement on page one of volume one, number one of *The Political Intelligencer and New Jersey Advertiser* on 14 October 1783, states:

HENRY LUPP.
GOLD AND SILVER-SMITH
In New Brunswich,
Makes and sells the following articles, in the modern and ancient mode:

Silver tankards, coffee and tea-pots, sugar pots and urns, pint and half pint cans, waiters, soup and punch ladles, sauce-boats and ladles, table, pap, dessert and tea spoons, shoe, knee and stock buckles, thimbles, sleeve - buttons, &, &, & . . .

Jewelery
Stone stock and knee buckles, locket buttons, gold lockets and buttons, ladies handkerchief slides, bosom pins, plain and garnet gold broaches, a great variety of gold rings, garnet ear-rings together with other things as usual.

N. B. Hair - work laid in the neatest manner.
October 13, 1783.

Henry Lupp used at least four types of marks each one consisting of H.L. in a rectangle and also H. Lupp in a rectangle.

During the first quarter of the nineteenth century, some New York silversmiths were listed as "thimble makers." An advertisement in the Philadelphia *Directory* of 1824 shows a workman at his bench and reads: "James Peters, gold and silver thimble and Pencil Case Manufacturer."

This was also the period of time when Providence, Rhode Island, became a center for the manufacture of all types of silverwork. Newark, New Jersey, was during this time the major American city for the manufacture of gold jewelry. Many gold thimbles that are thought to have been imported from Europe were actually made in Newark. Epaphras Hinsdale was the pioneer of this trade in 1801.

During this period of time, Long Island, New York, and New York City became extremely important to the manufacture of thimbles. In fact, New York City's first assay office and refinery was founded in 1834 by a company that made thimbles–Platt and Brothers.

Quite a large number of silversmiths came from Huntington, Long Island, during the first half of the nineteenth century. These men, instead of just making thimbles on order, had "ready made" thimbles on hand.

George Platt was listed in the New York Directories as a "Thimble maker." He was born on 2 August 1798 in Huntington. When he reached the proper age he was apprenticed to a New York City silversmith with whom he probably lived. He made his own tools with which to make thimbles and, in 1819, opened a shop with a partner; but this partnership lasted less than a year. He then went to another Huntington silversmith, Nathaniel Potter, for help. Nathaniel Potter was born on 23 December 1761. He started out in politics and was well known for his generosity to the town. He moved his silversmith shop to Huntington in 1820 when Platt and Potter were partners. Because of the inconvenience, this shop was moved to New York City in 1824. Platt bought out Potter's interest in the business and worked by himself until early in the year 1828. When his shop proved successful he took apprentices, including his brother. Nathan C. Platt was born on 20 December

1806. The shop was listed as G.W. and N.C. Platt, Jewelers, for a seven-year period.

The third silversmith in the Platt family, David, was born on 4 May 1801. In 1834 he also became a partner, and the name of the business was changed to Platt and Brothers. David left the business to become a farmer in Huntington in the year 1842. The name was changed to Platt and Brother, and the business was split into two parts—manufacturing and also assay and refining.

The Huntington Historical Society now owns a dainty gold thimble that was made by David Platt in 1828 for his wife Sarah. It is of yellow gold with red gold flowers and green gold leaves on the band. It is engraved "S. Platt" and, like most of the Platt's work, has no touchmark.

Eventually, Nathan took charge of the factory and management of "the store." His sons worked with him. They made thimbles, pencils and pencil cases, gold pens, spectacles, and watchcases, as well as silverware. A jewelry manufactory was added in 1850. As wholesale dealers, Platt and Brother bought merchandise from other American and foreign manufacturers.

The branch of business managed by George was "the refinery." There were fifteen employees, as well as his sons. Both branches of the business had customers in all parts of the United States and in Canada. By the middle of the nineteenth century they were well-established merchants in New York.

Nathan's personal business was taking up too much of his time; therefore, by 1853, all lines of manufacturing were discontinued except the jewelry. His foreman was placed in charge of the jewelry, but he did not have much artistic talent, so the line became "odd and old fashioned." After 1857, Platt and Brother did no more manufacturing.

Nathan became ill and suffered from business troubles. George, therefore, bought his brother's interest in the business so that Platt and Brother could not be held responsible for judgments against Nathan. In May of the year 1861, George resumed business under the name "George W. Platt." William Platt, Nathan's son, managed "the store" until 1863 when he left the business. His two brothers remained with their uncle until 1869. At that time the three brothers, as executors of Nathan's estate, brought suit against George for one-half the partnership's estimated worth of over $700,000 and all the other holdings that their father had owned. They claimed that their uncle had promised to return these holdings to their father. Before the case was settled in 1883 it had been appealed, with many changes. George died on 3 April 1881, and the executors of his estate became the defendents. It was finally resolved, with the plaintiffs being awarded half the partnership and its holdings as well as Nathan's other properties, which George had purchased at public auction. Until about 1915 the business remained in the family.

The Platt's touchmarks are listed as "Firm name, capitals in rectangle"—G.W. + N.C. Platt.

George Platt, in 1826, took his second cousin, Ezra Conklin Prime, as an apprentice. Prime was born on 20 December 1810. He was such an apt student that in 1831, when his apprenticeship was over, George offered to make him foreman of the shop. Toward the end of 1832, Prime formed a partnership with John Roshore. Ezra was an imaginatively creative man, but his nervous system could not keep pace with the force that drove him; therefore, he left the business to study. In 1837, Ezra Prime established a thimble factory in Huntington. Of his five brothers, three were also silversmiths and specialized in the manufacture of thimbles.

Edward, who was born on 12 December 1808, was also apprenticed to George Platt. In 1834 he formed a partnership with John Roshore. Ezra formed a company with John Roshore in 1849. Edward also was probably a member of this Prime, Roshore and Company. It was dissolved in the middle of 1850. Edward and Ezra Prime were associated for a period of time, during which they made thimbles in Huntington.

The third Prime brother who trained as a silversmith was Claudius. He was born on 11 February 1819 and learned the trade from Ezra. He probably worked for Roshore and Prime until 1848 when he established his own shop.

The youngest Prime silversmith was Nathaniel, known as Scudder, who was born on 19 August 1828. He also learned the craft from a brother and was probably a member of E.C. Prime and Company.

E.C. Prime and Company opened a jewelry store in Huntington on 10 May 1850. There they sold imported merchandise in addition to jewelry and silverware that they made. The store ceased operations in 1856. Edward left E.C. Prime and Company in 1853. He took Miles Griffith as a partner. In June 1857 his wife left him, taking their seven children and personal property with her.

Claudius, in 1859, formed a partnership with Scudder and George R. Rogers. As Prime Brothers and Rogers, they made thimbles. In 1867, Scudder made and sold "dentists' materials." Claudius continued alone, making "Gold, Silver and Steel Top Thimbles and Gold and Silver Shields, &." He returned to Huntington to manufacture thimbles in 1869 or 1870.

In 1859, Ezra Prime was supplying thimbles to dealers all over the United States and was also exporting them. "Ten or twelve men are constantly employed, and five or six gross of gold and silver thimbles are made daily." At the height of his success, Ezra, who has been called "the father of the thimble industry in America," was one of the largest thimble manufacturers in this country. When, after the middle of the nineteenth century, steam power was introduced to the manufacture of jewelry, Ezra was ready for the improvement with a larger factory. In the spring of 1864 he advertised for a boy "to learn the Thimble Makers trade."

By 1870 there were two thimble factories in Huntington. Claudius returned and entered into competition with his brother. He was an energetic man who developed cancer, but he filled orders for thimbles almost to the day he died in 1873. No thimbles were left in the shop to be included in the inventory. A statement against the estate by Scudder was for work done in May and June of that year:

To Making 145 doz. and 9/12th doz. silver thimbles at 20 cents	$29.15
Making 2½ doz. gold thimbles	$ 2.50
Rolling 28 bars at 10 cents	$ 2.80
Two hours work	$ .40
	$34.85

By 1871, Ezra's many enterprises overtaxed his nervous system and his doctors advised he rest. In June he was taken to an asylum in New York, but he was not treated kindly there. Because of his skill in working with metals, he was able to make a key out of wire. He let himself out and returned to Huntington but was returned to the asylum. After a few months he was discharged. Ezra then continued to expand the business, while his sons managed the farm. In 1883, "owing to an unfortunate mental affliction," Ezra was placed in a home. He died in 1898. After their father's confinement, Theodore and William operated the thimble factory. Gilbert T. Woglom, a manufacturing jeweler in New York, acted as "Sale Agents for 'Prime Thimbles' " until July of 1890 when the manufacture of thimbles was discontinued.

No evidence of a touchmark used by Ezra Prime or his three brothers has been found.

In the first part of the year 1832, John Roshore worked in the G.W. and N.C. Platt silversmith shop, but by the end of that year he established his own shop. He held a partnership with Ezra Prime and the Prime brothers for almost eighteen years. When the last of these partnerships dissolved by the middle of 1850, John formed a partnership with Brewster Wood, Jr. Brewster was a cousin of both the Platt and the Prime brothers. The Roshore and Wood Company dissolved in 1853, but Wood continued to make thimbles until 1865 when he gave up the business to become a hatter.

John Roshore's last partner was Edward Ketcham. Ketcham, who was born on 5 January 1820, learned the craft with him. Ketcham was also a first cousin of the Prime family and probably worked for Roshore and Prime until late in the year 1843.

A partnership was formed between Roshore and Ketcham as soon as the Roshore and Wood partnership broke up. This one lasted only a few years because John Roshore died.

At this point Edward Ketcham convinced his brother Ebenezer to join him in a New York shop. Ebenezer was another silversmith who probably learned the craft from Ezra Prime, about the year 1854. Ketcham and Brother, besides making thimbles, also manufactured gold cane heads, umbrella mounts, fancy ferrules for pipes, and similar gold and silver items that could be made with thimble-making machinery.

When the business took in a third partner, Hugh McDougall, the name changed to Ketcham, Brother and Company. McDougall was born on 23 July 1834 and learned silversmithing from Ezra Prime.

A new partnership was formed again in 1875 when Ebenezer Ketcham died. This new company, called Ketcham and McDougall, advertised "improved gold and silver thimbles." Hugh McDougall was an inventor as well as a silversmith, and in 1881 he filed a claim for "a novel method of making a thimble. . .so rolling a blank as to form a thick portion for the rim. . .also an embossed ornamentation." Some of the most beautiful thimbles made by Ketcham and McDougall have raised designs on the band. They were made by this new process. In 1882, McDougall invented "new and useful Improvements in the Art of Making Thimbles." These produced the same effect as the earlier method but probably at a reduced production cost.

The Ketcham and McDougall Company became the leading manufacturers of thimbles in New York. In fact, because thimbles were so important to this company, in 1850 it opened "The Thimble House." There, thimbles were the main business, not a side line. Other small sewing implements were also sold by them. Ketcham and McDougall were equalled by only one other nationally known company—that of Simons Brothers of Philadelphia.

Edward Ketcham died in 1894; but, following his wishes, his two sons formed a new partnership with Hugh McDougall. The old name of Ketcham and McDougall was retained. After several years McDougall retired from the business and in 1900 he died.

Still using the Ketcham and McDougall name, Hugh McDougall's sons assumed responsibility for the factory operation, while Edward Ketcham's sons carried on the sales office. In 1918 a corporate organization was formed. By the middle of the year 1931 the New York sales office was discontinued. The factory moved to East Orange, New Jersey, in 1939, but the manufacture of thimbles had been discontinued in 1932.

It was not until 1913 that a "trade-mark used on sewing thimbles" was registered by Ketcham and McDougall, but they stated it had "been used continuously in our business since the month of August, 1892." This mark, which is found on many thimbles, is composed of the initials **K + McD**, with the **K** somewhat larger than the other letters and centered between the **M** and the **D**. A small **C** is superimposed on the upper part of the stem of the **K**, and a plus sign (&) is at the bottom in the space between the stem and the lower prong of the **K**. The mark is always impressed on the inside of the thimble, on the underside of the apex.

Some thimbles are found that do not have a maker's mark but instead are marked "Pat. Sep. 20 '81." Since one with this marking is decorated with the same design that is drawn on Hugh McDougall's patent papers of that date, it seems safe to assume that any thimbles with that marking were made by Ketcham and McDougall between 20 September 1881 and August 1892, even though they do not have the proper trademark. No mark has been found that can be attributed to John Roshore, the founder of Ketcham and McDougall.

Other parts of the United States also had thimble-making silversmiths. Simons Brothers Company, one of the major thimble manufacturing companies in America (the only one that still is making gold and silver thimbles), was started by George Washington Simons in Philadelphia in the year 1839. His brother Peter B. Simons joined the firm in 1853 and in 1863 he went to San Francisco to open an office for the company. In the 1860s two other men, Thomas Maddock Jr. and Stacy B. Opdyke, served as partners in the company. In 1870 the name was changed to George W. Simons, Brother, Opdyke & Co. It was shortened to Simons, Opdyke & Co. in 1875. Opdyke left the company in 1876. In 1876 the company was honored by being awarded a Centennial Medal and Diploma for canes and thimbles.

George had four sons who were all in the business. The first to work with his father, in

1877, was Frederick M. Simons. In 1881 two older sons, John F. Simons and George W. Simons Jr., joined the firm. A third man, John T. Spiecker also joined that year and the company name was changed to Simons, Brother & Co.

In 1882 Peter B. Simons purchased the San Francisco branch from the company but still acted as an agent for their wares in a retail capacity. Also in 1882 George W. Simons' fourth son, Edward S. Simons, came to work for the company but he did not become a partner until 1888. In 1883 John Spiecker left the company.

Late in 1887 or early in 1888 George W. Simons died. A few months later, on 3 May 1888, George W. Simons Jr. died. The three remaining brothers, John, Frederick, and Edwin, formed a new partnership on June 1, 1888 but retained the same name. John F. Simons died on December 14, 1902.

The familiar Simons trademark, an escutcheon centered with an S in a simplified Old English lettering, was registered in 1907. They claimed to have used this mark "since the year 1880."

Frederick and Edwin formed a corporation in 1913 and changed the name to Simons Brothers Company, which it is still called today. Edwin served as manager at the New York sales office. The company also had representatives in Chicago, San Francisco, and Toronto. Edwin retired in May of 1928 and died on 26 January 1929. Frederick continued as the president of the company until March of 1935 when he died.

Frederick's daughter, Lillian Lesley Simons, took over the leadership of the company until she died in 1945. Then her sister Katherine W. Simons became the president. She was in charge until her death in August of 1968. Katherine's niece, Elizabeth Bassett, ran the company until she sold it on 12 September 1969 to Nelson Keyser. Mr. Keyser, who started out at Simons Brothers as an apprentice, and his family still run the company.

Over the years Simons Brothers has made many items other than their famous thimbles. Included in this list are: canes, umbrella and whip mountings, gold pencils, chains and charms, fine jewelry, silverware, toilet articles, hollowware, flatware, and novelties of precious metals. One of these items of which they are very proud is the presentation sword that was given by the city of Philadelphia. A famous one was given to General Meade at the end of the Civil War.

Simons Brothers also operated a retail jewelry store for a time and were dealers in watches and diamonds.

Until the Korean War Simons Brothers also made thimbles of nickel. These were not marked with the familiar Simons S in the shield but instead had the letters S. B. C. in a keystone shaped shield.

Providence, Rhode Island, at one time, also had a firm that manufactured thimbles. It was founded by Jabez Gorham, who lived from 1792 until 1869. He first made thimbles as a boy when he was apprenticed to Nehemiah Dodge, who in 1794 founded the first jewelry business in Providence. In 1813, Gorham became a master jeweler. In the early 1830s he had a shop where, with partners named Webster and Price, silver thimbles were made. They also manufactured spoons and jewelry there.

12 SILVER AND THE SILVERSMITH

THE majority of thimbles that the collector is able to find today are of silver; therefore, some information about this metal and the process by which the craftsmen learned how to use it is of interest.

Silver is an element that by itself is too soft to be used practically. This problem of ductility was overcome by using a small amount of strengthening copper as an additive or alloy with the pure silver. The proportions used in this mixture varied, producing different grades of silver.

Coin silver, with 900 parts pure silver to 100 parts copper, was the grade used for minting coins in the United States. In the early days of our history, people had the habit of taking their coins to the silversmith who melted them down and made various items, including thimbles, out of the resulting molten silver. To the colonists this was the equivalent of keeping money in a bank. If financial difficulties arose, the product would be melted down again and reformed into coinage. In this practice, it was quite rare for the silversmith to stamp the piece with the word "coin." Sometimes "pure silver" was used. This was put on coin-grade silver.

The most used grade of silver is that known as the "sterling" standard. This has 925 parts pure silver to 75 parts copper, so it actually is 25 points higher in silver than coin. For centuries, sterling has been recognized as the ideal quality of silver for all uses. After 1860 it was–and still is–common practice to stamp the silver object with the word *Sterling.*

The English and Continental standards differ from those of the United States. In the eighteenth and early nineteenth centuries, they used 75 parts copper and 925 parts pure silver, the same as our sterling. But in 1840 the standard was changed to 100 parts copper alloy to 900 parts pure silver. Many Continental pieces have the mark *800* on them. This means that the item has either 880 parts silver to 120 parts copper or, from Scandinavia or Germany, 830 parts silver to 170 parts alloy; therefore, if a thimble is found to have an 800 mark, it is not of American manufacture.

In colonial times, the silversmith was a highly trained craftsman. A young boy who was to learn the trade started his education in the craft at about the age of twelve years. He left his family and went to live with the master of the craft. This apprenticeship usually lasted for seven years, as it took that long to become proficient in the techniques of the silversmith. Often the craft was passed down from father to son, as evidenced by the two Paul Reveres.

For the young apprentice the working of silver became a part of his daily life. He had to develop a feel for the metal and the forms into which it could be shaped. The methods of decoration applicable to silver had to become part of his nature.

The workshop where the silversmith worked was usually quite small and insignificant looking. It was often built right onto the master craftsman's house.

Among the many things the apprentice learned in those small shops was how to use the tools of the silversmith. In an inventory of tools that belonged to John Burt of Boston, who died in 1745, the following was listed: "1 Thimble stamp £4.10/ 6 pr. of flasks for casting £4.10. . .9."

Silversmiths in America were often called upon to make thimbles to the order of their customers. Often a thimble was one of the first objects a young man learned to make because it was fairly easy and took a small quantity of silver.

The raw silver was melted down and refined. The molten silver was poured into a mold or ingot. This was then hammered into a sheet of the required thickness. A circular piece equal to the outside dimensions of the object to be made was then cut. Because silver became brittle as it cooled, an annealing process was necessary during the entire operation. This was done by means of a charcoal fire that was fanned by hand-operated bellows. The form of the piece was brought into being by successive hammering. Tools called gravers were then used to incise the decorative details. Finally, burnishing stones were used to hand polish the entire surface.

Thimbles, in considerable numbers, were made by the smiths, but unfortunately not very many survived. Because of their small size they were easily lost and also had little intrinsic value because they required such a small amount of the metal. And, as was often the case, many may have been melted down and made into other objects.

A short list of some of the types of decoration used to embelish objects of silver will be helpful to the collector.

DECORATIVE PROCESSES

ENGRAVING—The removal of part of the metal by gouging with a shaving tool no matter how small the amount removed might be. Engraving includes lettering, armorial bearings, and decorative or symbolic devices.

BRIGHT-CUT ENGRAVING—Done in the late eighteenth and early nineteenth century. It was made from a succession of broad shallow side cuts of the tool. It produced numerous small facets at a slight angle.

CHASING—A design made with punches. None of the metal is removed. Sometimes a slight burr is raised which is burnished off afterwards.

FLAT—Chasing shallow punch marks.

MOLDING—Casting in molds such parts as it is not convenient or suitable to work up with a hammer or fashion over shaped anvils.

FILLETING—An application of bands, rims, and decoration moldings.

GADROONING—Producing a series of convex gadroons or nulling by working up sheet metal or a piece of hollow-ware over a shaping anvil or mold shaped for the purpose.

EMBOSSING OR REPOUSSE WORK—Amplification of gadrooning, production of more than one motif. Beak irons are placed inside the vessel. Hammering from the outside over them produce a raised design.

STAMPING—Stamped by dies in a strip of decoration which is then soldered in place.

All kinds of letters are used, from Roman capitals to many varieties of script. The letters are well spaced, well proportioned, and graceful.

Some of the common decorative features used on silver include foliage, scrolls (foliated and flowered), cherub's heads, garlands, and ribbons.

Waffle top. "EVA." James E. Pim, London. Very bright cut chasing. C. 1889. (F)

*Sterling–England. Zigzag swirl band; hallmarks, "S*FS Birmingham." 1902. (D)*

Sterling–England. Waffle top; hallmarks in apex, "J.E.P. JAS. E. PIM." Chester and London. 1889. (E)

Sterling–England. Waffle band, hallmarks. J.F. Birmingham. 1889. (D)

Sterling–England. Zigzag geometric band; hallmarks, "C.H. Chester." 1886. (D)

Sterling–England. Faceted rim; hallmarks, "C.H. Chester." 1898. (D)

Sterling–England. Hallmarks, "C.H. Chester." Date not readable. (D)

Sterling–England. Allover design; hallmarks, "C.H. Chester." 1901. (E)

Sterling–Birmingham, England. Maker's mark, "JF"; engraved "A.W.L. from E.M.A.D." 1835. (E)

Sterling, size 3. Maker's mark, "SF;" Chester "Pat. 19157"; finger shaped with nail defined. 1872. (E)

Sterling–England. Domed crown; all-over design; sides; roses; band; hallmarks, Chester C.H." 1897. (E)

Sterling. Raised all-over design including swirls. Simons Bros. (E)

Sterling. Feathers top and plain band. Simons Bros. (E)

Sterling, size 6. Raised scrolls and band. Simons Bros. (E)

Sterling. All-over design; beaded rim. Ketcham and McDougall. C. 1880. (E)

Sterling. Feathers top and paneled band. Simons Bros. (E)

Silver. All-over swirl design; beading over rim. Simons Bros. C. 1880. (E)

Silver. All-over design, four-leaf clover in circles. C. 1900. (E)

English sterling. All-over design. C. 1880. (E)

Sterling. All-over design marked "PAT. 10, R^{d}127211." (E)

Sterling. All-over design. "Prov Pat NON SLIP." C. 1900. (E)

Sterling—Paris. Made by Louis Antoine Taillepied, 1750-1756. (F)

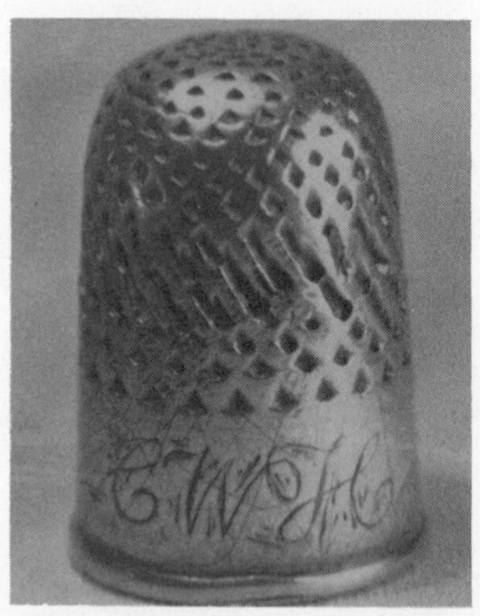

Coin silver. Handmade. Note triangular pouncing; inscribed "C.W.H." Middle eighteenth century. (E)

Coin silver. Handmade. Note triangular pouncing. Inscribed "C.W.H." Eighteenth century. (E)

Sterling, size 9. Raised cherubs and garlands; "Pat. Nov 21 '05." Simons Bros. (G)

Sterling. Shield on side marked "12," believed to be eighteenth century from Philadelphia. (E)

Sterling. Zigzag geometric band; raised fleur-de-lis rim; inscribed "M.H.W." Early nineteenth century. (E)

Sterling. Raised cherubs and flowers band (three different poses). Ketcham and McDougall. (E)

Sterling. Applied banner and two cupids on band; anchor mark. (E)

Sterling. Liberty Bell. "Proclaim liberty in the land by order of the assembly." Simons Bros. (E)

Sterling. Scene. "Washington D. C." Capital, White House, and Washington Monument. Simons Bros. (E)

Sterling, size 5. "A Stitch in Time Saves Nine." Simons Bros. (F)

Sterling. Commemorative of Salem witch trials. Design by Daniel Low. Pat. September 18, 1902. Ketcham and McDougall. (E)

Sterling. Applied roccoco band; uneven rim. Ketcham and McDougall. C. 1890. (E)

Sterling. Scene (raised): sunset, buffalo, horses and riders, campfire, trees, Conastoga wagon, and locomotive. Simons Bros. (E)

Sterling. Eight raised fleur-de-lis on band. Simons Bros. (D)

Silver, European. Applied geranium leaf band; scalloped rim line. (E)

Sterling. Raised vintage band. Simons Bros. (E)

Sterling. Christmas bells, holly and berries band. Simons Bros. (E)

Sterling. Raised feathers and flowers band. Simons Bros. (E)

Sterling. Openwork lattice and raised band. Simons Bros. (E)

Sterling. Raised diamonds on rim; in apex "Diamond" anchor mark. (D)

Sterling. Flower and circle band raised swirl rim; anchor mark. (E)

Sterling. Raised scroll rim. Ketcham and McDougall. (C)

Silver–England. Square pouncing; flower band; maker's mark "C H"–Charles Horner; "DORCAS." Dorcas thimbles are silver with a steel lining to add strength. Hence they can not have sterling's hallmarks. They were sold with a lifetime guarantee. (E)

Silver–England. Square pouncing; inscribed "M. W."; maker's mark "C H"–Charles Horner; "Little Dorcas." This was another name used for the steel lined silver thimble. (E)

Silver–England. Maker's mark "H. G. + S."–Henry Griffith and Sons; "Dreema" Dreema thimbles, like Dorcas thimbles, have a steel lining for added strength. (E)

Sterling salesman's sample on cork No. 32. Used for ordering from the salesman. (D)

Sterling, size 8. Buildings, footbridge, pump, and mountains. Simons Bros. (E)

Sterling. Scene: silo, stone bridge and village. Simons Bros. (D)

Sterling, scenic. Farm scene: sunrise, field, barn, trees, mountains; feathers rim. Simons Bros. (D)

Sterling, scenic. Castle, houses, and bridge; feathers rim. Simons Bros. (D)

Sterling, scenic. Harbor scene: boat, lighthouse, village; beaded rim; anchor mark. (D)

Sterling, scenic. Stone arched bridge, sailboat, lighthouse, houses, and mountains; feathers rim. Thomas S. Brogan. (D)

Seaside scene with lighthouse. Brogan. C. 1900. (E)

Sterling, scenic. Viking ship, lighthouse, castle, church, mountains; slashed rim. Gunner Mfg. (D)

Stone arched bridge. Brogan. C. 1900. (E)

Sterling, scenic. Stone bridge and cathedral with stained-glass window; inscribed "M.T." (D)

Sterling, scenic. Village, mountains, and bridge; feathers rim. Simons Bros. (D)

Sterling, scenic. Village: grass, pebbled sky, slashed rim; inscribed "M.W." (D)

Coin. Castle scene; beaded rim. C. 1860. (F)

Sterling, scenic. Castle, towers, and portcullis; beaded rim. (D)

Coin. Castle scene; beaded rim. C. 1860. (F)

Simons family collection–Gold with yellow enamel. Design of pink roses, green leaves, and blue butterflies.

Meissen–iron-red trellis ground with squared quatrefoil panels of figures in landscapes. German. 18th century.

Meissen–with Watteau scenes in Kupfergrun between Regence lappets. German. 18th century.

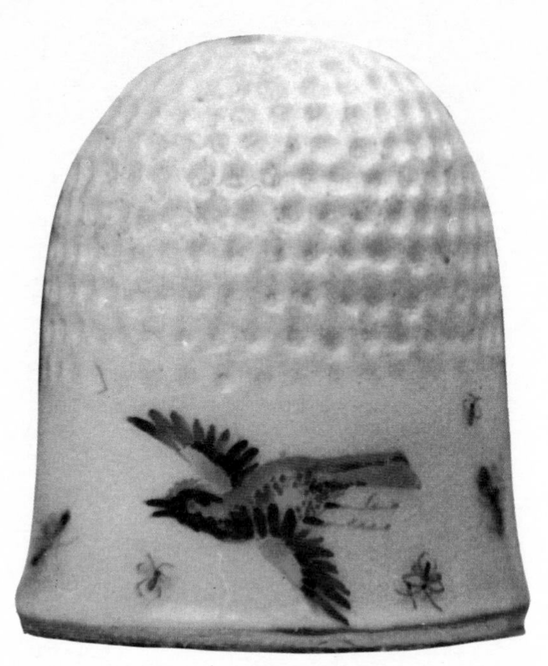

Meissen–painted by J. E. Stadler with birds and insects in the oriental style. German. 18th century.

Simons family collection–Gold with enamel (red, blue, and green) and jewels (diamonds and rubies).

Meissen–dentil in the manner of Hauer with figures in a continuous harbour scene. German. 18th century.

Meissen–pale turquoise border reserved with a pastoral scene in purple. German. 18th century.

Meissen–continuous JAGD landscape with a horseman pursuing a boar and other figures among dense trees. German. 18th century.

Meissen-continuous harbour landscape by B. G. Hauer. German. 18th century.

Simons family collection–Gold with party-color band showing bird, flowers, and leaves in high relief.

Meissen–seeded turquoise waist with panels of oriental flowers, the rim with iron-trellis and the top with flower sprays. German. 18th century.

Enamel on sterling–pink and blue flowers and green leaves. Simons Bros. This thimble was a sample. Note that it is still on the cork which held the style number. It was made by Mr. Herman.

Meissen–Continuous border of figures in the manner of J. G. Herold, seated at two tables with children and flowers. German. 18th century.

Meissen–continuous border of figures in the manner of J. G. Herold, seated at a table and with vases, bird lures, and a bird cage. German. 18th century.

Coin. Castle scene. Early Simons. (F)

Sterling, scenic. Unusual combination of building and floral band. (D)

Sterling, scenic. Small ovals with different buildings in each. (D)

Sterling, size 6. Wild rose. Ketcham and McDougall. (D)

Sterling, floral. Bleeding heart. C. 1900. (E)

Sterling, floral. Orchid and scrolls on ribbed background. Webster Co. (D)

Sterling, floral. Raised ovals with flowers between them. Simons Bros. (E)

Sterling, floral. Daisy and leaves (has a goldish color). Webster Company. (E)

Sterling, floral. Bird, bee, and flowers; ovals on rim; anchor mark. (E)

Sterling. Two birds and flowers band. Feathers rim. Simons Bros. (D)

Sterling. Flowers and leaves band. Ribbed rim. Simons Bros. (D)

Sterling. Birds and flowers on band. C. 1900. (E)

Sterling, floral. Flowers and leaves on vine; feathers rim. Simons Bros. (D)

Sterling. Raised daisy band. Simons Bros. (D)

Sterling, floral. Vintage band; inscribed "C.A." (D)

Sterling, vintage. C. 1870. Note diagonal pouncing. (E)

Sterling, Art Nouveau. Deliah beaded rim. C. 1910. (E)

Sterling, floral. Lillies-of-the-valley scrolls on background; beaded rim. Ketcham and McDougall. (E)

Sterling. Wildflowers; diagonal ribbed rim. C. 1900. (E)

Silver. Mixed flowers on band; beaded rim. C. 1900. (D)

Sterling. Ivy leaf and dots; beaded rim. C. 1900. (D)

Sterling. Cactus leaf; beaded rim. C. 1900. (D)

Sterling. Art Deco floral band. C. 1920. (D)

Sterling. Cactus leaf band. C. 1900. (D)

Sterling, floral band. Ketcham and McDougall. (D)

Sterling, floral. Vine of leaves; crown mark. (D)

Sterling, floral band, Faceted rim. Ketcham and McDougall. Inscribed "Ethel." (D)

Sterling. Diagonal floral; striped band. (C)

Sterling. Shamrock on ribbed background. C. 1900. (E)

Sterling, floral. Flowers and indented hexagons in circles on band. Simons Bros. (D)

Sterling. Abstract flower band. C. 1900. (D)

Sterling, floral. Daisies in shields; crown mark. (D)

Sterling, floral. Flowers and ferns on band. Ketcham and McDougall. C. 1880. (D)

Sterling. Asters on band. Simons Bros. (D)

Sterling, "World's Columbian Exposition 1492-1892" souvenir. The exposition was held in Chicago in 1893 because the buildings were not completed on time. (E)

Sterling. Small flower band. Simons Bros. (C)

Sterling. "NEEDLECRAFT." Beaded snail band; feathers rim; anchor mark. (D)

Sterling. Rare advertising: "Chalmers Pearls." (E)

Sterling. Souvenir "Yellowstone" Tongue and dart band. Simons Bros. (D)

Silver. Advertising: "WENIGER & Co.," Philadelphia. C. 1920. (D)

Sterling. Advertising "Maison Blaiche" Simons Bros. (D)

Sterling. "Century of Progress Chicago 1934" Feathers rim. Simons Bros. (E)

Sterling. Advertising "W. C. Munn Co. Houston Tex." Simons Bros. (D)

Sterling. Anchor band; feathers rim; star mark. This is the ideal thimble to be used in the boat-shaped holders of shell with bisque sailor boy riding in the boat. (E)

Sterling, size 11. Engraved "E.L." Simons Bros. (D)

Sterling. Arch-topped band; feathers rim. Simons Bros. (E)

Sterling. Feathers and diamonds; beaded rim. C. 1890. (E)

Sterling, size 5. Engraved "A.L.W." (D)

Sterling geometric band. Rib and leaf rim. Ketcham and McDougall. (D)

Sterling medalion band. Feathers rim; inscribed "W." (D)

Sterling. Diamond and swirl band. Simons Bros. (D)

Sterling geometric band. Ribbed background; beaded rim. Simons Bros. (D)

Sterling. Leaves in shield band. Simons Bros. (D)

Sterling. Feathers and shell band; inscribed "M.H." Ketcham and McDougall. (D)

Sterling. Feather band and feather rim. C. 1900. (E)

Sterling. Acanthus leaf; beaded rim. C. 1900. (E)

Sterling. Feathers and feathers. C. 1900. (E)

Sterling. Palmate band; beaded rim. C. 1900. (D)

Sterling. Feathers and feathers. (D)

Silver. Palmate band. C. 1900. (D)

Sterling. Roccoco band. C. 1900. (E)

Sterling. Pattern called "Priscilia" marked in apex "Pat May 31 '98." Simons Bros. 1898. (D)

Sterling. Paneled band; alternating plain and different decorated panels. (D)

Sterling. Paneled band with leaves and shaped rim. Simons Bros. (E)

Sterling. Paneled band with shields and circles. Simons Bros. (D)

Sterling. Paneled band with diamonds. (D)

Sterling. Flowers on paneled band. Simons. C. 1900. (D)

Sterling. Paneled band. Simons Bros. (D)

Sterling. Paneled band with two flowers. Simons Bros. (E)

Sterling. Paneled band; acanthus leaves. Webster Co. (D)

Sterling. Paneled band with different designs. Note diamond pouncing. Ketcham and McDougall. (D)

Sterling. Diamond pouncing; paneled band with different designs. C. 1900. (E)

Sterling. Paneled band; diamond pouncing. C. 1910. (D)

Sterling. Arched panels. C. 1900. (E)

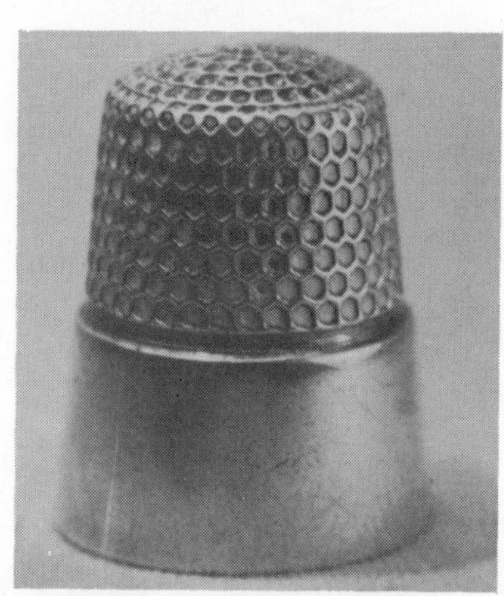

Sterling. Quaker lady's thimble. A Quaker could use this thimble because it is absolutely plain. Thomas S. Brogan. (D)

Sterling. Paneled band with dotted shields. Simons Bros. (D)

Sterling Quaker band. (C)

Sterling Quaker band. Inscribed "C.M.S." Simons Bros. (D)

Sterling Quaker band. Inscribed "Eleanor." Ketcham and McDougall. (D)

Sterling. "4 H" "Clothing achievement winner 1952." Simons Bros. (D)

Greek key, right hand. Simons. C. 1910. (D)

Greek key band. Inscribed "C.C." Simons Bros. (D)

Greek key, rarer left hand. K & MD. C. 1910. (D)

Sterling. Diamond pouncing and diamond band. Simons Bros. (D)

Sterling. Gothic arches over stars. C. 1890. (E)

Sterling. Diamond pouncing and waves band. Simons Bros. (D)

Sterling. Swirls and dots band. (C)

Silver. Feathers and cubes. C. 1900. (D)

Sterling. Flowered circle and ovals band. Simons Bros. (D)

Sterling. Diamonds and circle band. Simons Bros. (D)

Sterling. Acanthus leaf. C. 1900. (D)

Sterling. Cròss and dot band; crown mark. (D)

Sterling. Swirl band. Simons Bros. (C)

Sterling. Scallops and dots band. Simons Bros. (D)

Sterling. Feathers and circles band; anchor mark. (D)

Coin silver. Lincoln drape. C. 1865. (F)

Coin silver, American. Beaded; rickrack band. C. 1860. (F)

Coin silver. C. 1870. (E)

Coin silver. Plaid band. C. 1870. (E)

Coin silver. Rolling hills. C. 1860. (E)

Coin silver. Hills and valleys. C. 1870. (E)

Coin silver. Geometric triangle band; note diamond to circle pouncing. C. 1860. (E)

Coin silver. Marked coin is unusual: "A.L. & Co." (E)

Coin silver. Plain band; B in diamond mark. (C)

Palmate band. "Muntz." C. 1900. (D)

Sterling. Swirls on band. (C)

800 mark; European. Diagonal ribbed and beaded; C. 1920. (D)

Sterling. Small palmate border. (C)

Sterling. Palmate band; indented slashed rim. (D)

Sterling. Beaded snail; faceted and ribbed rim; Ketcham and McDougall C. 1910. (D)

Beading on band. (C)

Sterling. Herringbone band. Simons Bros. (C)

Sterling. Art Deco. C. 1920. Ketcham and McDougall. (D)

Sterling. Small dot and triangle band; anchor mark. (C)

Sterling. Palmate band; inscribed "S. Miller." (C)

Sterling. Ocean waves. C. 1910. (D)

Sterling. Palmate band; inscribed "Fannie." (C)

Sterling. Palmate border. (C)

Sterling. Double palmate band; inscribed "M.A." (B)

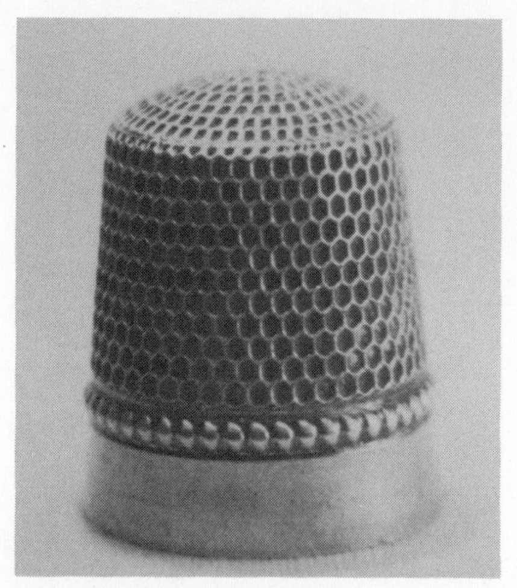

Sterling. Beaded top band; honeycomb pouncing marked "SC"; anchor mark. (D)

Small panels. Simons Bros. C. 1920. (D)

Sterling. Inscribed "Blanche 1886." (D)

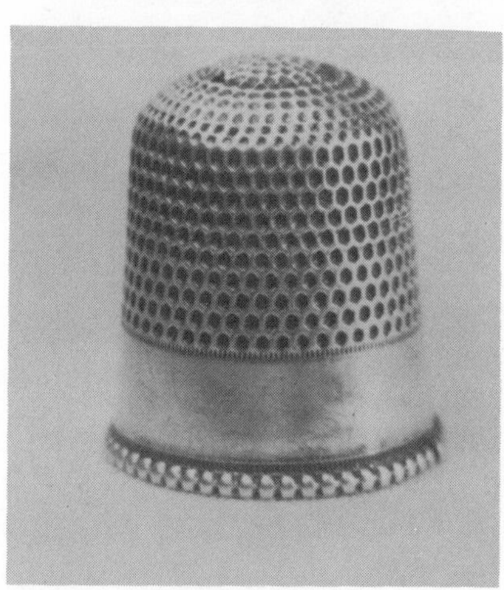

Sterling. Beaded rim. (C)

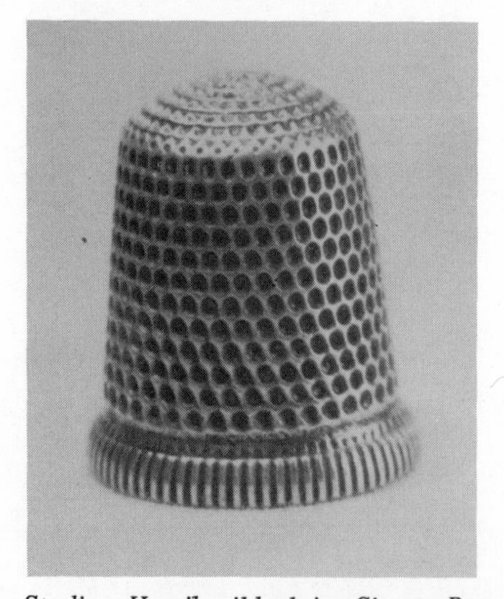

Sterling. Heavily ribbed rim. Simons Bros. (C)

Sterling. Ribbed band. (B)

Sterling. Small star band; anchor mark. (B)

Sterling. Upper ribbed band. Simons Bros. (B)

Sterling. Ribbed band; diagonal ribbed rim. (B)

Sterling. Small palmate band. (B)

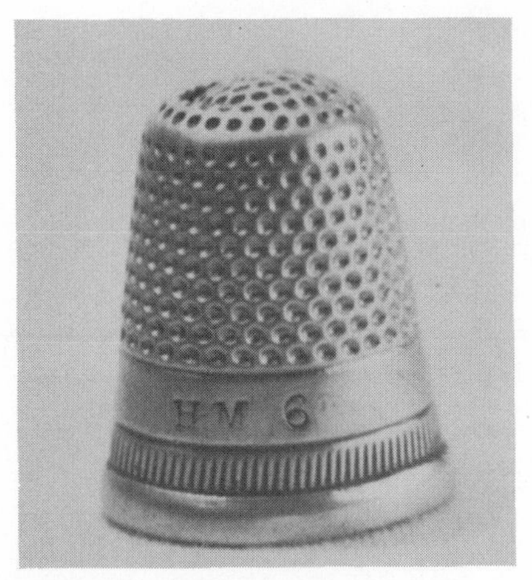

Sterling. Small ribbed band; inscribed "C.R.R."; mark, "HM." (B)

Sterling. Minute pouncing; faceted rim. (C)

Plain silver. (C)

Utility silver. (C)

13 GOLD

SEWERS have always enjoyed the rich feeling that using a thimble of gold gives. Since the early days of thimble making, the wealthy have had gold thimbles made for their wives and other favored women. Gold thimbles have been made in many different styles including some set with jewels and others with enamel. The gift of a gold thimble always made a woman feel very special.

Gold–England. Set with turquoise and rose diamonds. Nineteenth century. (K)

Gold–England. Set with turquoise. Nineteenth century. (K)

Gold–England. Turquoise enamel. Nineteenth century. (K)

Gold–England. Set with jewels: three diamonds, one ruby, one emerald, one sapphire. Nineteenth century. (K)

Gold–England. Parti-colored gold band, shield on side. C. 1820. (I)

Gold–England. Black enamel, acanthus leaf rim, inscribed "M.W.," diamond pouncing. Nineteenth century. (K)

Gold. Eight large panels, four plain, four different designs. Note small area of pouncing. (H)

Gold. Scenic band: boat, sailor, birds, cattails; stars and circles rim. Simons Bros. Inscribed "J.M.H." (G)

Gold. Village scene band; feathers rim; inscribed "A.L.T." (G)

Gold-American. Scenes are rarely this detailed in gold. "MJP." March 8, 1874. (H)

Gold. Scene: lighthouse and sailing ship on ocean. "A. K." Simons Bros. (G)

Gold. Scene: barns and silo. "E. R. S." Simons Bros. (G)

Gold. Small paneled flower band. Simons Bros. (G)

Gold. Vintage band. Feathers rim. Simons Bros. (G)

Gold. Ivy vine band; diamond rim; inscribed "Edna." (G)

Gold. Vintage band; swirls rim; inscribed "L.A.H." (G)

Gold. Oak leaf band; arrowpoint rim; inscribed "M.L.L." (G)

Gold Childs thimble. Feathers band; beaded rim; very fine detail work. C. 1840. (G)

Gold. Floral garland on ribbed background; two bands of tiny beading. Simons Bros. (G)

Gold. Feathers band. Simons Bros. Inscribed "M.D." (G)

Gold. Floral garlands and bows on ribbed band. Simons Bros. (G)

Gold. Feathers on band. Simons Bros. (G)

Gold. Geometric triangle band; triple band rim; diamond pouncing; inscribed "L.P.D." (G)

Gold. Vesica band. Feathers rim; inscribed "L.B." (G)

Gold. Vesica band; feathers rim. (G)

Gold. Diamond and oval band; feathers rim; anchor mark. (G)

Gold. Greek Key band; inscribed "P.R.F. to E.V.N. 20." (G)

Pink gold. Gothic Arches band; zigzag.

Gold. Ovals on swirl background band. "M. C. W." Simons Bros. (G)

Gold. Band of ribs and two rows of garlands. Simons Bros. (G)

Gold. Leaves on paneled band. Simons Bros. (G)

Gold. Band of diamonds and two rows of Greek Key. Simons Bros. (G)

Gold. Inscribed "Mrs D. I. Clark 1839 Mar 28th 1889." Fiftieth anniversary present, 1889. (G)

Gold. Band of diamonds and two rows of garlands. Simons Bros. (G)

Gold (10 K). Faceted rim; anchor mark. (G)

Gold Childs size. Feathers rim. Simons Bros. Inscribed "Frances." (G)

Gold. Feathers rim. Star mark. (G)

Gold. Feathers rim. Simons Bros. Inscribed "C.C.H." (G)

Gold. Feathers rim; inscribed "E.R. Jenckes." (G)

Gold. Feathers rim. Ketcham and McDougall. (G)

14 IVORY AND BONE

AMONG the many materials from which thimbles have been made include ivory and bone. Ivory thimbles have been made since ancient times and may have first been used by the Chinese. Often the ivory is decorated with a delicate lathe design. The indentations are handmade. Ivory thimbles are smooth and pleasant to use.

The shape of the ivory does not give a valid indication of the date when the thimble was made. They have been made during the last three or four centuries. The shapes can either be short with a separate flat top or long and tapering with a domed top. They were made according to the fashion of the time or perhaps just the whim of the maker.

Some thimbles of ivory, and others of horn or tortoiseshell, were made without indentations. These were used on the first finger of the left hand as finger guards. They protected the finger from the continual prick of the needle's point.

A different type of ivory thimble is of scrimshaw. They were popular in New England during the peak of the whaling days. On the whaling ships, the teeth of the captured whale were distributed to the sailors. During their leisure hours the sailors carefully carved the teeth into useful objects to be given as gifts when the ship returned to port. Sewing items were often carved in this manner. After the carving was completed, a design was often delicately embossed into the ivory with a fine-pointed tool. This design was then rubbed with lamp black to make it stand out against the delicate pale color of the ivory.

Ivory, very old. Made with separate crown piece, handmade indentations. (F)

Ivory. Carved by scrimshaw artisan. Modern. (D)

Vegetable ivory. Hand carved. Nineteenth century. (E)

15 CHINA AND PORCELAIN

IN the eighteenth century some thimbles were made of porcelain. They were made of Dresden porcelain, and in England, of Chelsea, Derby, and Royal Worcester porcelain. They were usually white and often had a painted design and gold-color trim.

By the second quarter of the nineteenth century, thimbles of bone china, which was stronger and tougher than the earlier soft-paste porcelain, were extremely popular and were made in quantity. Those made by Royal Worcester had the company's mark on them. They had an indented top, but the sides were smooth to allow for the decoration—usually a design of birds or flowers.

These china thimbles were often given as gifts. They were too fragile for general use; therefore, they were displayed in cabinets or corner cupboards. But when the ladies sewed on silk, the china thimbles were used because of their smoothness. This was a bonus, as there were no irregularities to snag the fine threads and make pulls in the fabric.

Meissen Porcelain, Germany. Large chinoiserie, yellow border, with two quatrefoil panels of a man fishing with a duck and a man baiting an animal, in the manner of J. G. Herold, eighteenth century. (L)

Meissen porcelain, Germany, with three Ogival landscape panels on iron-red ground with guilt border. Eighteenth century. (L)

Meissen porcelain, Germany. Large iron-red trellis ground with squared quatrefoil panels of figures in landscapes. Eighteenth century. (L)

Meissen porcelain, Germany. Dentil with harbor scene border, green trellis band, "Mon coeur est a vous" *in iron-red and guilt star. Eighteenth century. (L)*

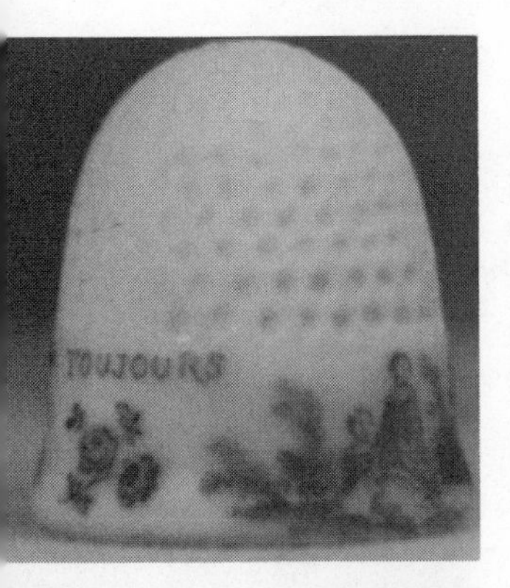

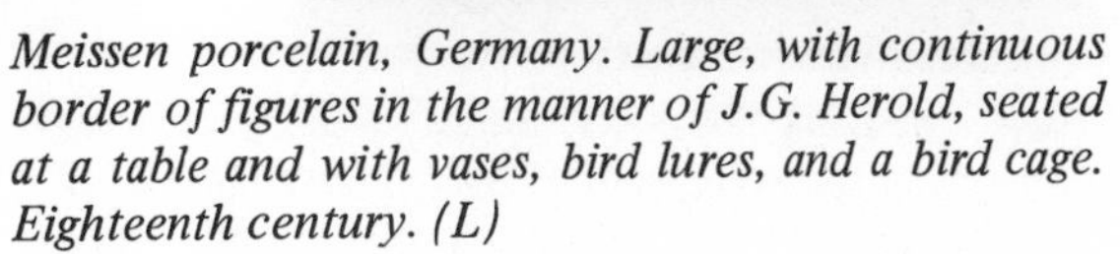

Meissen porcelain, Germany. Large, with continuous border of figures in the manner of J.G. Herold, seated at a table and with vases, bird lures, and a bird cage. Eighteenth century. (L)

Meissen porcelain, Germany, with Watteau scenes, green flowers, and inscription "Toujours devoue a vous." *Eighteenth century. (L)*

Meissen porcelain, Germany. Small, of Clemens August type, painted by C. F. Herold, vignettes above "Laub-und' Bandelue," *and inscription* "Je pense a vous." *Eighteenth century. (L)*

Meissen porcelain, Germany. Small, with continuous border of figures in the manner of J.G. Herold, seated at two tables with children and flowers. Eighteenth century. (L)

Meissen porcelain, Germany, with continuous JAGD landscape with a horseman pursuing a boar and other figures among dense trees. Eighteenth century. (L)

Meissen porcelain, Germany. Large, with continuous harbor landscape by B.G. Haver. Eighteenth century. (L)

Meissen porcelain, Germany. Dentil, in the manner of B.G. Haver, with figures in a continuous harbor scene, scalloped edge. Eighteenth century. (L)

Meissen porcelain, Germany. Large, painted by J.E. Stadler, with birds and insects in the Oriental style. Eighteenth century. (L)

Meissen porcelain, Germany. Small, the pale turquoise border reserved with a pastoral scene in purple. Eighteenth century. (L)

Meissen porcelain, Germany. Seeded turquoise waist with panels of Oriental flowers, the rim with iron-red trellis and the top with flower sprays. Eighteenth century. (L)

Meissen porcelain, Germany. Watteau scenes in Kupergrun between Regence lappets. Eighteenth century. (L)

China–England. Hand-painted birds, gilt borders. Nineteenth century. (E)

China–England. Hand-painted bird and flowers, gilt borders. Nineteenth century. (E)

Bone china, England. Modern Spode, blue band, gold cherubs, gold design on crown. (C)

Bone china, England. Unmarked Royal Worcester, bluebird, and purple flowers. Early nineteenth century. (F)

Back of early Royal Worcester.

Bone china, England. Royal Worcester, marked inside. Hand-painted pink rose, signed D. Res. First quarter twentieth century. (D)

Bone china, England. Modern Royal Worcester, mark on back. Design called "Bride's Thimble." (B)

Back of Royal Worcester showing artist's signature.

Back showing Royal Worcester mark.

China–France. Modern Limoges, small blue and purple flowers. (B)

China–Holland. Blue Delft. Modern. (A)

Bisque–Germany. Pale pink, signed inside–Stimes. C. 1900. (E)

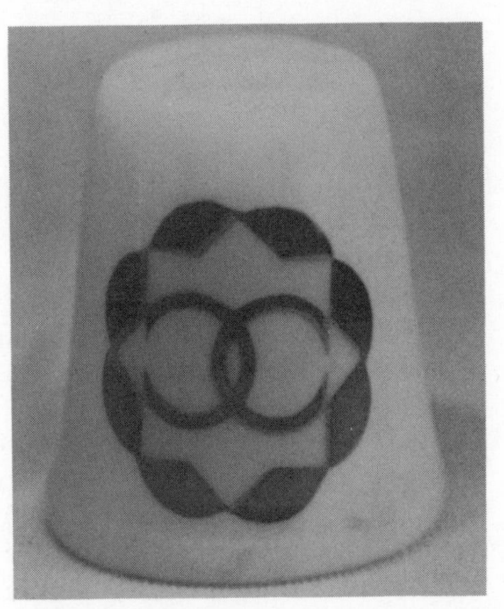

China. Yellow and gold logo of Collector's Circle thimble collector's club. 1976. (C)

Modern thimble, "Blue Onion" design. Signed Hahnny. (B)

16 JEWELS AND STONE TOPS

MANY of the most beautiful thimbles are decorated with jewels; others have hard-stone tops. Modern thimbles often have synthetic stones. Older thimbles, frequently from the eighteenth century, may have semiprecious stones such as sardonyx, moss agate, carnelian, amethyst, onyx, turquoise, jade, avanturine, coral, abalone, moonstone, and topaz. An interesting theory is that these stones were used with a double meaning. The obvious one was their beauty. But it is possible that the stones were chosen with their amuletlike powers in mind. If this is true, some interesting combinations were used; for example, sardonyx was thought to be a protection against witchcraft and also to protect the health of the eyes. Eyesight was certainly important to the seamstress. Moss agates also were believed to protect the eyes. Carnilian was a help in keeping the skin healthy (women have always had some vanity). Amethyst brought gentleness. Onyx was used to protect against the evil eye, and, of great importance, was thought to be influencial in easing the birth of a child. Turquoise was lucky and protected against poison and eye disease.

These indented caps were made and supplied by lapidaries. They were mounted in bezels on the top of the thimble. The fine indentations on the metal sides of these thimbles were used for light sewing; the stone tops, for more stubborn material. On the older of these jewel-topped thimbles the jewel is backed by a solid metal apex.

Another type of jewel-enhanced thimble has a series of small jewels set around the band. Among the jewels used for this type of design were coral, turquoise, and abalone.

A third type of jeweled thimble is made totally of the mineral. Thimbles carved from a solid block of onyx are an example. They had smooth sides and an indented top. One of the prettiest of this type is the French-made mother-of-pearl thimble. It often has narrow gold rims around the band, and some also have small gold pansies inlaid into the mother-of-pearl. This kind of thimble was made in the late 1700s and early 1800s. It was often part of a whole set of mother-of-pearl and gold sewing implements that was made to fit into the compartmented shelf of the sewing boxes, which were so popular during that period. Similar thimbles were made of tortoiseshell.

Onyx. Carved from single piece; white shaded strata. (E)

Sterling. Amethyst top, shields and garlands on band; bottom of band oxidized; arrow rim. C. 1890. (G)

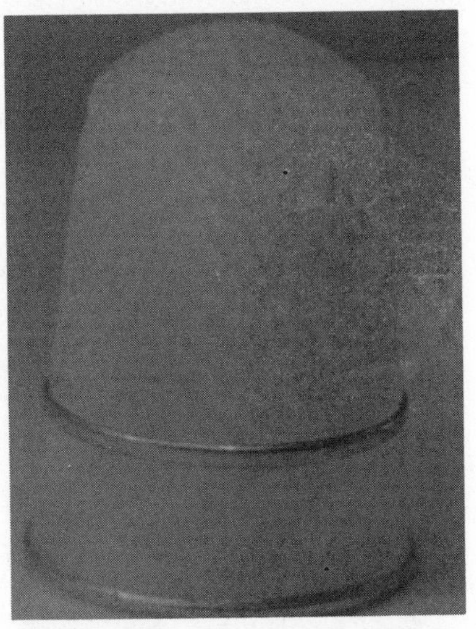

Mother-of-Pearl. Gold bands around rim. French c. 1780. (H)

Sterling (800)–Germany. Pale amethyst top, shield on side, "T" on shield, circles and commas on rim. C. 1890. (F)

Sterling–England. Blue mother-of-pearl top; hall-marks maker C.H. Chester; raised stars on rim, flower designs on sides. 1902. (F)

Sterling. Amthyst top. Flower band. European. (F)

Sterling (800)–Germany. Carnelian (red) stone top, shield on side. C. 1890. (F)

Sterling–Norway. Light green synthetic stone top, band of stylized flowers on side. Modern. (D)

Silver. Topaz stone top, palmate in shield band, diagonal ribbed rim. C. 1880. (F)

Sterling–Denmark. Synthetic blue stone, marked "HJ" on apex. Modern. (D)

Sterling. Synthetic red stone top, inscribed "J.A.R." Modern. (D)

Sterling–Denmark. Synthetic royal blue stone top; mark in apex–H.J. (D)

European. Petticoat band (flaired), turquoise. Rare design. C. 1880. (G)

Sterling (800). Six turquoise stones of varying shades, arranged light to dark; bought in Paris. C. 1890. (E)

Sterling (800). Five polished coral stones; Italian styling. C. 1890. (E)

Italian-style jewel band; green and pink semiprecious stones. C. 1890. (F)

Sterling (800). Gold lined and gold band; six green stones. C. 1890. (E)

17 ENAMELS

THIMBLES made of silver and copper are sometimes decorated with bands of enamel. This practice started in England at Battersea during the seventeenth century. Battersea thimbles were made of copper, with decorative enamel in bright colors applied to the outside. A piece of brass was sometimes put into the apex to help withstand the pressure of the needle. Often, thimble cases were also made of Battersea enamel.

About the year 1770 in South Staffordshire and Birmingham, silver thimbles with enameled bands were produced. The enamel decoration often had flowers or tiny motifs. Many were made in a souvenir style, showing scenes of the place visited. An example would be the blue and white bands depicting Dutch windmills and ships.

Enamel-decorated thimbles were made in many countries. Beautiful-flowered ones were produced in Germany. Intricate designs in white and turquoise enamel were made in Russia and Sweden. The American thimble-manufacturing firm, Simons Brothers, made several enamel designs.

Some of these enameled thimbles were made twice as beautiful by the use of a gemstone apex. Moonstones were often used, but other jewels including jade were also used. Some enameled thimbles are still being manufactured, including some with stone tops.

Copper. Enamel: orange with pink roses and green leaves. (E)

Sterling (800)–Germany. Enamel: cream background, red roses, green leaves. Made by Gabler (company disbanded in 1963). (E)

Sterling. Enamel background pale green with blue and pink flowers and green leaves; white enamel bands on top and bottom. Simons Bros. C. 1900. (E)

Sterling–Germany. Enamel: pale blue background, red roses, green leaves, gold dots. (E)

Sterling. Enamel: pale blue background, thirteen pink roses, green leaves. (E)

Sterling–Germany. Enamel: blue background, three pink roses, two white daisies with yellow centers. (E)

Sterling 800 mark "JW." Enamel: blue and white scene of windmill buildings, birds, boats, trees. Feathers rim. (E)

Back of blue and white enamel.

Sterling and enamel. Enamel Masonic symbol (blue and white). Ribbed rim. Simons Bros. (E)

Sterling and Enamel. Enamel "red cross" feathers rim. Simons Bros. (E)

Sterling–Germany. Moonstone top. Enamel: pale blue background with red roses, green leaves, gold scallops. (F)

Sterling–Germany. Green stone top. Enamel: dark green background with pale green shamrocks. (F)

Sterling with gold wash, Sweden. Moonstone top. Enamel: turquoise and white (F).

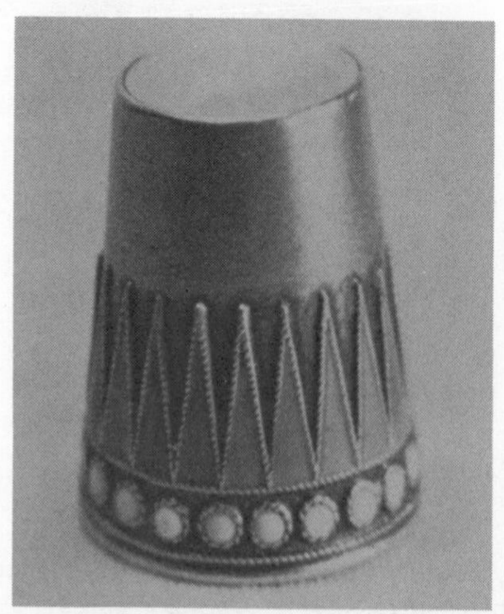

Sterling, Sweden. Moonstone top. Enamel: turquoise and white. (F)

Sterling with gold wash, Sweden. Moonstone top. Enamel: turquoise and white. (F)

18 BRASS

BRASS has always been a metal used to make thimbles. Archaeological digs have uncovered important thimbles made of brass as well as silver thimbles. As a metal with less intrinsic value than silver, brass was a common material for thimbles intended for everyday use. When they wore out after much hard use, they could be discarded without much monetary loss. Although utilitarian, brass thimbles vary in design; some have nicely decorated bands and others are quite plain.

Brass. Swans and swamp grass band. (D)

Brass finger guard. No pouncing. Used on hand under embroidery to protect against needle's point. (C)

Brass–Germany. Hearts on band. (B)

Brass "Friendship" band. Stars rim. (C)

Brass. Flower band; slashed rim. (B)

Brass, child's size. "Industry" band. (C)

Brass. Flowers and leaves band; slashed rim. (B)

Brass–Austria. Palmate shield band. (B)

Brass. Greek key design; slashed rim. (B)

Brass–Austria. Basket weave band. (B)

Brass. Advertising "Clarks O.N.T. Cotton." O.N.T. means "Our New Thread." (B)

Brass. Shields on band. (B)

Brass. Triple band. (A)

Brass–England. "Her Majesty" thimble. (D)

Brass. Two tiers. (A)

Brass–Japan. (A)

Brass–England. (B)

Brass–Germany. Three tiers. (B)

Brass–Germany. (B)

Brass. Heavy; cross mark. (C)

Brass. (A)

Brass–England. (B)

Brass. (A)

Brass. Heavy. (A)

Brass–Japan. (A)

19 SOUVENIRS

IN the early part of the Victorian era, many thimbles were made to be sold to the increasing number of tourists who were traveling more because of the improvements in transportation. These souvenir thimbles often were decorated with representations, sometimes in relief, of famous buildings, bridges, and other well-known landmarks.

The decorated sides of the thimble were stamped separately, using a die, from a flat piece of silver. This was then rolled and seamed. It was then soldered to the upper, functional part of the thimble.

These souvenir thimbles were popular in Europe and also here in America. Some examples of the British souvenir thimble include The Tower of London, St. Paul's Cathedral, London Bridge, and Buckingham Palace. Smaller cities and tourist attractions also had thimbles made, to act as reminders of a pleasant vacation for their owners.

Events also were commemorated by special thimbles. The Great Exhibition of 1861 was a popular theme. Another, the "Exhibitions of All Nations 1851," shows a picture of the Glass Palace on an enameled band. The "International Exhibition 1862" shows the Victoria and Albert Museum on an enameled band.

Many thimbles were made with the Royal Family as their subject. Examples include the engagement of Victoria and Albert, using their pictures in an oval and a rose and thistle decoration; Queen Victoria, "Crowned June 28, 1835," with a crown and a rose and thistle decoration; "Prince Royal Born at Buckingham Palace, November 21st, 1840," with a picture of the Queen and an angel with an infant prince; "Jubilee 1887"; "The Diamond Jubilee of Queen Victoria, 1837-1897"; Silver Jubilee 1910-1935, King George V Queen Mary" and a crown; "E R 1953" for the coronation of Queen Elizabeth II, using horses and coach, London Bridge, and an angel with a trumpet.

The patriotism of the English during Victoria's reign was also shown with thimbles that give a list of dates that every citizen was expected to know; thus, the needlewoman could learn while she worked on her sampler or comforter. These lists were as follows:

Queen Victoria Born	May 24, 1819
Ascended the Throne	June 20, 1837
Crowned	June 28, 1838
Married Pc. Albert	Feb. 10, 1840
Princess Royal born	Nov. 21, 1840

Some were kept up to date with the addition

"Christened at Buckingham Palace Feb. 10, 1841."

Other European thimbles were popular as souvenirs; many had enameled bands or an enameled shield with the name of the city and a typical symbol of it. Venice could have a gondola on a canal, Rome a picture of the Colosseum, Paris the Eiffel Tower, Lourdes a representation of the shrine, Australia a kangaroo, Switzerland with William Tell's Chapel, Easter lilies from Bermuda, and thistles from Scotland.

Some of these souvenirs were representative of the locale in other ways. Carved bog-oak thimbles came from Erin, with shamrocks and sometimes the name "Killarney." Onyx thimbles came from Mexico, some with colored flowers and "Pueblo." One type of metal thimble had a small hole in the dome, which shows scenes of the area when held up to the light—a kind of "peep show."

Souvenir thimbles were also popular in the United States, and many were made with American themes. Some of these were historic, such as a World War Liberty Bell engraved "Proclaim liberty in the land to the inhabitants—by order of the Assembly of Pennsylvania in Philadelphia, 1752," made by Simons Brothers of Philadelphia. There were also World's Fair thimbles from Chicago in 1892 and thimbles from the World's Columbian Exposition 1492-1892 with exposition buildings. A thimble from the St. Louis World's Fair in 1904 had a buffalo, Indians, a canoe, signal fire, Conestoga wagon, locomotive engine, trees, and the sun setting in the west. The original was made by Simons Brothers and may have had lettering. Copies were later made that had no lettering.

Other American souvenirs include the exposition at Philadelphia in 1926, marked "Sesqui-Centennial 1776—Philadelphia—1926" by Simons; and "Century of Progress, Chicago 1934," also by Simons.

States also had thimbles, such as one with an alligator from Florida and one from Hawaii with a seal in 1949. Palm Springs, Florida, had one with palm trees. Salem, Massachusetts, had its witch trials commemorated by a Ketcham and McDougall thimble showing "Salem 1692" in raised letters with a quarter moon, a witch with broom, a cat, and a cauldron. "St. Augustine, Fla. Settled 1565" in raised letters and a coat of arms was also made by Ketcham and McDougall. "Washington, D.C.," has a picture of the White House. "Homestead Hot Springs, Va.," has a picture of the hotel. "Merced General Hosp. Merced, Calif.," shows the hospital. One with "Battle of Plattsburg, September 11, 1814, Lake Champlain" shows the lake and ships. Another has "Rocky Mountain—Big Horn Sheep from Grand Lake—Colorado."

Enamel is also used in the United States. A Washington, D.C., souvenir has the entire side completely enameled with a picture of the White House and another of the Washington Monument. One from Yellowstone Park has a park seal. Another has an enameled shield with red and white stripes in the lower part and a blue ground with white stars in the upper part, on an engraved band with an anchor on each side. This particular thimble came in a wooden case bearing a transfer print of Bunker Hill Monument on the lid. The thimble was made by Goldsmith, Stern and Company in New York.

A whole new array of American souvenir thimbles was inspired by the celebration of the Bicentennial of the American Revolution in 1976. These have values from only a few dollars to almost a hundred dollars for elaborately enameled ones. Many collectors are accumulating numerous examples of these in the hope that they will increase greatly in value in the future.

Sterling, bicentennial. "American Bicentennial of Freedom 1776-1976." Simons Bros. (D)

Glass, bicentennial. Eagle on front; "1776-1976" on back. (C)

Gold tone metal, bicentennial. Cloisonné design; red, white, and blue; "1776-1976." (A)

Gold-tone metal, bicentennial. Cloisonné design; red, white, and blue; "1776-1976." (A)

20 TAILOR AND RING-STYLE THIMBLES

THIMBLES without tops are called tailor's thimbles. They were used by tailors because they allowed the finger tip to feel the texture of the fabric. Also, dropped pins could be picked up more easily. Women find this style of thimble pleasant to use because it allows long finger nails to extend and not be hindered by the crown of the thimble. Because of the different sewers who use this type of thimble, tailor's thimbles are found that are large and of heavy duty metals, and others are found that are smaller and of precious metals and are nicely decorated.

Another type of topless thimble is the ring thimble used in Asian countries. It is an indented ring of metal that is the same width all around or an under layer of metal or plastic with an upper layer of indented leather. This style thimble is worn above the second joint of the finger. The needle is pushed with the side as it is with the tailor's style thimble.

Sterling, tailor's, size 10. Engraved "I.W." (D)

Sterling, tailor's. Beaded snail band; slashed rim. (C)

Sterling, tailor's. Paneled band, infrequent in tailor style. C. 1890. (E)

Sterling, tailor's. Ribbed. C. 1900. (D)

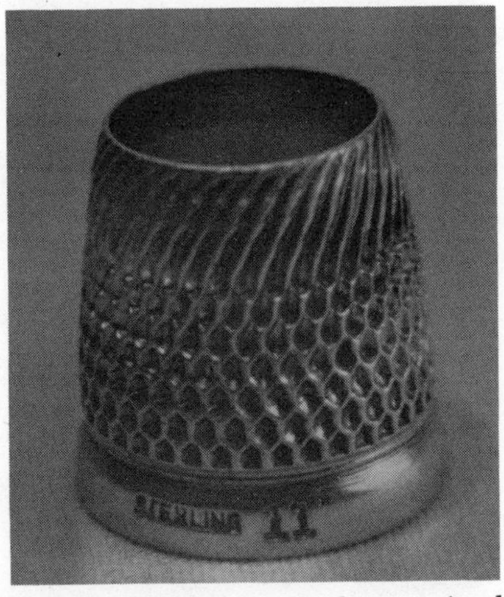

Sterling, tailor's. Note honeycomb pouncing leading to diagonal ribs. (C)

Silver, tailor's. Tongue and dart. C. 1870. (D)

Sterling, tailor's. Note honeycomb pouncing. (D)

Silver, tailor's. Palmate band; graduated size of pouncing. C. 1900. (D)

Silver, tailor's. (B)

Tailor's. Iron with brass liner and band. C. 1900. (C)

Nickel-lined with brass, tailor's. Brass rim; child's size. (B)

Metal, tailor's. (A)

White metal, tailor's. Small palmate band. (B)

Heavy iron, tailor's. Crude seam. (B)

Tailor's. Heavy steel lined with aluminum. (B)

Tailor's. Steel lined with brass; hand-punched indentations; crude join on side. (D)

Brass. Asian ring thimble. (C)

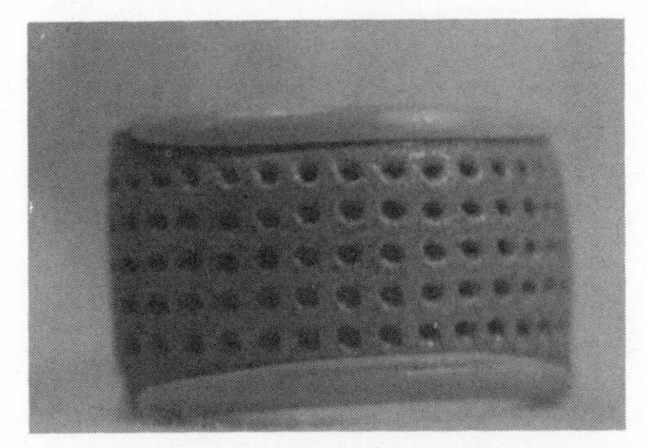

Leather and Plastic. Asian ring thimble. Red plastic. (C)

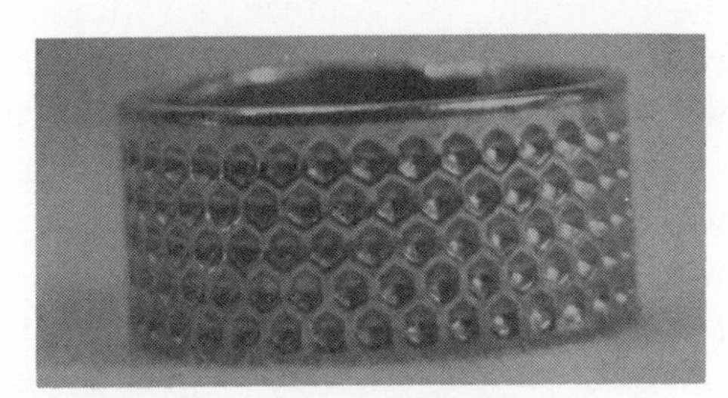

White metal. Asian ring thimble. (C)

21 ADVERTISING THIMBLES

ONE of the most easily obtainable kind of thimble is the advertising thimble. Advertising thimbles were made on order for a company or business, with a slogan, name of the company, the company's address, or any combination of the three. These thimbles were then given away by the company to customers or potential customers. The idea was that whenever the thimble was used, the wording would remind the user of the company and its services. And since the thimble was an item that was used frequently, the idea of the advertising thimble was used by many businesses of all sizes. Companies with a nationwide reputation used advertising thimbles, as did local, small-town businesses. Usually, advertising thimbles were made of an inexpensive material and, therefore, made up in large quantities, the financial outlay for the business was relatively small in comparison to the amount of public recognition the thimbles brought.

An outgrowth of the advertising thimble is the political thimble. This was made in the same way, except instead of making known a business it was used to promote a political candidate. These thimbles were distributed in hopes of gaining votes for the candidate in the same way that campaign buttons were hoped to draw votes. Candidates for national office, including president of the United States, and candidates for local-government posts used thimbles to promote their chances. Two presidential campaigns that used thimbles were the successful 1924 Republican Calvin Coolidge and Charles G. Dawes team and the 1928 successful Republican team of Herbert C. Hoover and Charles Curtis. This team ran again in 1932, but this time they lost. Thimbles have been used for Congressional campaigns; one of the best known was Richard M. Nixon's campaign for senator. The thimble says "Nixon for Senator."

State government races also used thimbles to bring their candidates to the notice of the public. Races for governor, state assemblys, and state senates used political thimbles.

Some of these political thimbles in their slogans told who the candidate was and for what office he was running. Others just told the candidate's name and assumed the public knew the office, such as "Vote For Kalteissen & Layden." One in the author's collection just says "Who is Sam Orr?"

These political and advertising thimbles were most often made from a material that would cost the person or business being advertised a small amount; therefore, it is quite rare to find an advertising thimble made from a precious metal. One example of such a thimble is marked "Sterling" and advertises "Chalmers Pearls." Probably the reasoning behind the use of such a costly metal in an advertising thimble was that pearls are an expensive item and the people who have the money to consider purchasing pearls would be more likely to use a silver thimble than one of a lesser material. Using the thimble would remind the sewer of the virtues of Chalmers Pearls.

Another metal that is used for advertising thimbles only occasionally is brass. Among the many kinds of advertising sewing items it used, Clark Thread Company gave away brass advertising thimbles saying "Clarks O.N.T. Cotton." The "O.N.T." in their slogan stands for Our New Thread.

One of the earliest common materials used for manufacturing advertising thimbles was celluloid. Celluloid was a forerunner of the plastics of today. It is an artificial substance that is made from vegetable fibrin and was often used as a substitute for ivory or bone. Many celluloid thimbles are found to have on the apex "B + B St. Paul, U.S.A." This was a company that made celluloid thimbles in this country. Others are marked "Germany." One celluloid advertising thimble with an effective slogan was made for the "Wertz Implement Co." They had "A Thimble Full of Friendliness" imprinted over the company name.

With the discovery of plastics, many advertising thimbles came to be manufactured with this inexpensive material. Another advantage of plastic was the wide range of vivid colors available. Vivid colors were helpful because the thimbles drew the eye to their brightness, and the idea of an advertising thimble was for it to be seen and its message, therefore, remembered.

Plastic thimbles are found that advertise many kinds of businesses and services. The range is just about endless as is the area in which the advertiser is known. Some were made for small local businesses, such as one for "Star Cleaners Launderers Long Branch 6-4700."–this one is from Long Branch, N.J. Others were for nationally known firms and therefore do not give any address. Examples include "Tastykake" and "Singer Sewing Machines." Some just have a symbol such as the "4H" four-leaf clover.

Plastic thimbles were also made by the B + B company in St. Paul. Other plastic thimbles are just marked U.S.A., and still others have no marks at all. Any marks that are found are in the apex. If size numbers are used they are also in the apex.

The other material that is often used for advertising thimbles is aluminum. Aluminum is a white metal that has great strength, lightness, and is nontarnishing and nonpoisonous. It is easily formed into the thimble shape. Many advertising thimbles of aluminum have a band of color around the bottom, with the wording raised and left unpainted so the letters show up clearly. The Prudential and John Hancock Life Insurance Companies, however, have raised letters but no color band on their thimbles.

The colors most frequently used on aluminum thimbles are red, royal blue, navy blue, green, and black. Some have two-color bands such as red over blue. Examples of thimbles with red bands include "Singer Sewing Machines," "Equitable Life Ins. Co.," and "Enna Jettic Shoes $5-$6." This intrigued the author, so she wrote to the Enna Jettick company and they replied that the year during which their shoes sold for $5.00 and $6.00 was 1930.

Blue bands are found on thimbles advertising "White Sewing Machines," "Ask For The 'O.T.C.' Oyster Cracker," and "Taylor Pork Roll–New York World's Fair 1939." That particular one has interest to the World's Fair souvenir collector, as well as to the thimble collector.

"ButterNut 'the Coffee Delicious' " and "Drink House Of Lords Tea" are among the thimbles with green bands. "C. G. Larosh, Jeweler, 527 N. 7th" is one with a black band.

Most aluminum thimbles have no marks on them to indicate their manufacturer. The only one found with a size marking is not an advertising thimble but an aluminum one with a flower and vine border. A few aluminum advertising thimbles are impressed with the word "Austria." One example that was made in Austria was probably made for a Scottish firm, for it bears the slogan "Bonnie Laddie Shoes For Boys For Girls" and also has an outline figure of a person wearing kilts. One plain nonadvertising aluminum thimble is marked "Germany."

Sometimes a company used a larger advertising budget and gave out a sewing kit instead of a thimble alone. It contains a thimble that sits on top of a spool that held white and black thread and had a space for needles in the center. These parts fit into a case that had the advertising on it. A favorite of the author says "Lydia E. Pinkham's Vegetable Compound, Blood Medicine, Sanative Wash, Liver Pills."

Many of these advertising sewing items were used by companies that wanted to concentrate on getting their message across to the woman who would usually be the person to use the thimble. Examples include sewing machines, fabrics, foods, soaps, and hosiery. But others are found that advertise products that are not generally associated with women. Examples would be "Glenwood Vulcanizing Co." and "Holland Furnaces Make Warm Friends." Perhaps these companies counted on women being able to influence the buying habits of men.

Celluloid. Whitish green printing, "A Thimble Full of Friendliness WERTZ IMPLEMENT CO."; apex mark "B+B St. Paul USA." (A)

Celluloid. Tan; "Ryan's Dairy." (A)

Celluloid. White; design of cupids and garlands with blue ribbons; "The Cupid." (B)

Celluloid. Dark blue. (A)

Plastic. Light blue. Note square pouncing. (A)

Plastic. Transparent amber. (A)

Plastic. Bright blue; raised ribs; square pouncing. (A)

Plastic. Shades of blue in marbled effect. (A)

Plastic–Japan. Red. (A)

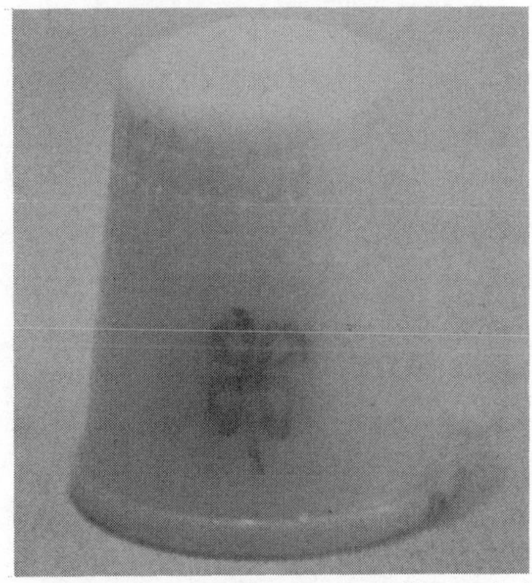

Plastic. United States. Off-white, green 4H symbol. (A)

Plastic. United States. White, blue design; "Tasty-kake." (A)

Plastic. White, blue and red printing; "Star Cleaners Launderers Long Branch 6-4700." (A)

Plastic. Ivory color bottom, red top; "Dogs Like KASCO Dog Ration." (A)

Plastic. White, blue letters; "Dugan's Bakers for the home," apex "B+B St. Paul USA." (A)

Plastic. White, black printing; "Cullen Photo Supplies 720 Bloomfield Ave Montclair." (A)

Plastic, United States. Off-white, red lettering; "Strawbery Banke Portsmouth N.H." (A)

Plastic. United States. Pink; "SINGER." (A)

Plastic. Bright yellow. Advertising "The Chase P. Withrow Agency 223-3232" (A)

Plastic. United States. White; "Singer Sewing Machines." (A)

Aluminum. Red band; advertising, "SINGER Sewing Machines." (A)

Plastic. United States. Yellow; "GRANTS FASHION FABRICS." (A)

Aluminum. Blue band; advertising, "Save in a Savings Bank." (A)

Aluminum. Red band; advertising, "Star Cleaners Humboldt 9321." (A)

Aluminum. Blue band; advertising, "666." (A)

Aluminum. Green band; advertising, "Larabee's Best Flour." (A)

Aluminum. Red band; advertising, "Enna Jettick Shoes $5-$6." 1930. (A)

Aluminum. Raised lettering; advertising, "The Prudential Life Insurance." (A)

Aluminum. Dark blue band; advertising, "Whiteking Soap." (A)

Aluminum. Blue band; advertising, "Glenwood Vulcanizing Co." (A)

Aluminum. Blue band; advertising, "New York World's Fair 1939 Taylor Pork Roll"; apex, "USA." (B)

Aluminum. Austria. Dark green band; advertising, "Bonnie Laddie Shoes for Boys Girls." (A)

Aluminum. Red band; advertising, "Holland Furnaces make warm friends." (A)

Aluminum. Blue band; advertising, "Ask for the O.T.C. Oyster Cracker." (A)

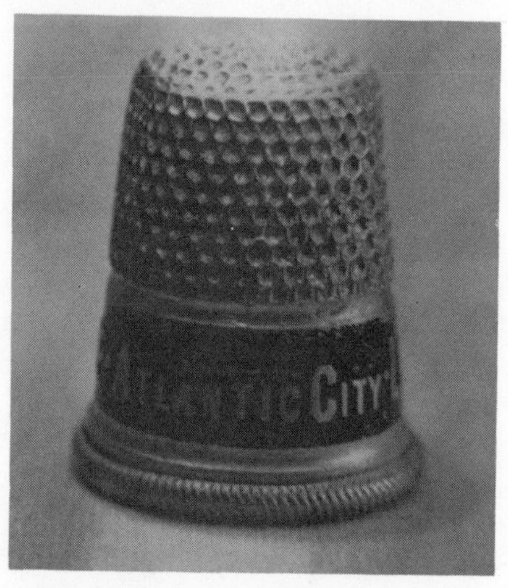

Aluminum. Dark blue band; advertising, "Lee's Curiosity Shop Atlantic City." (A)

Aluminum. Green band; advertising, "Prizer Ranges." (A)

Aluminum. Blue band; advertising, "Washington National Insurance Company." (A)

Aluminum. Blue band; advertising, "Unit Laundry uses Ivory Soap." (A)

Aluminum. Red band; advertising, "Boston Mutual Life Ins. Co." (A)

Aluminum. Austria. Green band; advertising, "Drink House of Lords Tea." (A)

Aluminum. Green band; advertising, "ButterNut the coffee delicious." (A)

Aluminum. Blue band; advertising, "White Sewing Machines"; apex, "B+B St. P." (A)

Aluminum. Austria. Blue band; advertising, "Drink He-No Tea." (A)

Aluminum. Blue band; advertising, "Borden's Grade 'A' Milk for Health." (A)

Aluminum. Blue band; advertising, "Real Silk Hosiery Mills Indianapolis Indiana" came in Milady's Mending kit especially for mending silk hosiery. (A)

Aluminum. Ribbed background; advertising, "John Hancock Muti Life Ins. Co - Boston." (A)

Aluminum. Red band; advertising, "Equitable Life Ins. Co." (A)

Aluminum. Currant vine band. (A)

Aluminum. Yellow band; advertising, "Lipton's Tea is Best." (A)

Aluminum. Flower band; ribbed rim. (A)

Aluminum. Ribbed rim; "Germz." (A)

Aluminum. Black band; political thimble for local election: "Vote for Kalteissen and Layden." (A)

Aluminum. Fine indentations. (A)

Aluminum. Blue band; political thimble for presidential election: "Coolidge and Dawes," 1924. (B)

Aluminum. Ribbed band. (A)

Aluminum. Blue band; political thimble for presidential election: "Hoover and Curtis," 1928. (B)

Aluminum. Red and blue band; political thimble for state election: "Whitney for Governor." (B)

Aluminum. Blue band; political thimble for state election: "Kean for Senator." Apex–B + B St. P. (B)

Aluminum. Blue band; political thimble: "Who is Sam Orr." (A)

Aluminum. Blue band; political thimble for state election: "Harper for Senator–Paid for by Baird-Harper Club." (A)

Aluminum. Pale blue band, blue lining; political thimble for state election: "Baird Business Man for Governor." (A)

Plastic. Pale blue; political thimble: "Re-elect Holman Member of Assembly." (A)

Plastic. Yellow; political thimble: "Vote for a Republican, Arthur J. May for Representative." (A)

Plastic. Cream; political thimble: "Everything is 'Fine'–Vote Duff and Fine." Apex–B + B, St. Paul, U.S.A. (A)

22 CHILDREN'S THIMBLES

IN hunting old thimbles, many small ones are found. These often cause the assumption that our ancestor's fingers were more pointed and smaller than ours. But this is not so. Many people today forget that young girls were brought up in a different manner before our modern age. Needlework was a "proper and genteel" pastime for women. A young lady's education was not considered complete until she had mastered these arts and knew how to make small decorative pieces of wearing apparel as well as useful household objects. Purely decorative embroidery was also very popular. For this education a young girl needed a thimble.

Nests of thimbles were made for children. They consisted of a number of small thimbles: the smallest might have been less than 3/8 inch in diameter at the rim, one fitting on top of another, gradually increasing in size to allow for growth. A child, by the age of seven or eight, was expected to be able to embroider an elaborate sampler; therefore, stitchery instruction began at a very early age. There are examples from the nineteenth century of samplers worked with plain letters and numerals by children only four years old. A small silver thimble about the right size for a child of that age is impressed with the motto "Forget-me-not." Other texts were also used, such as "For a good girl."

These child-size thimbles should not be confused with salesmen's samples, which were usually made of an inferior metal and were only meant to indicate the shape and pattern of available larger thimbles.

A thimble was often the first trinket a little girl would own. Thimbles were allowed long before she was able to wear personal jewelry such as a necklace, bracelet, or pin. Children's thimbles were often engraved. Designs include stars, flowers, and scenes. Some have an inscription around the rim giving the name or initials of the donor and/or the recipient.

Sometimes a special thimble was awarded upon the completion of a sampler that attained a degree of perfection that merited praise. It could also have been an inducement towards future efforts.

When a girl reached the age of fifteen an elaborate thimble was the traditional gift to recognize her maturity and also as a tribute to her accomplishments as a needlewoman.

Another time when a thimble was the proper gift was as a prelude to a girl's engagement. When the man was a craftsman, his gift to his future bride was a display of his skill in his own particular material.

Sometimes this engagement thimble was of the type called a "wedding band" thimble. It had a silver top and a gold band and was often rather tall. At the time of the marriage the gold band was cut off the top and was used as the wedding ring.

Sterling. Child's size. "The Cow Jumped Over the Moon." Cat and fiddle, moon, and cow. Simons Bros. (E)

Sterling, child's. Extremely tiny (3/8"), perhaps for a doll. (C)

Brass, child's. Well used. (B)

Sterling, child's. Very small, 7/16". (B)

White metal, child's. Two definite mold marks. (A)

Lead, child's. Two mold marks; "For a Good Girl" printed on both sides. (B)

Aluminum, child's. (A)

Aluminum, child's. Target band; slashed rim. (A)

White metal, child's. (A)

Aluminum, child's. (A)

White celluloid, child's. (A)

Brass, child's, England. Target band. (B)

Brass, child's. (A)

Aluminum, child's. Painted black band. goosey nursery rhyme. (A)

Child's. Narrow fan band; slashed rim. (C)

Sterling. Circles and bars band. (C)

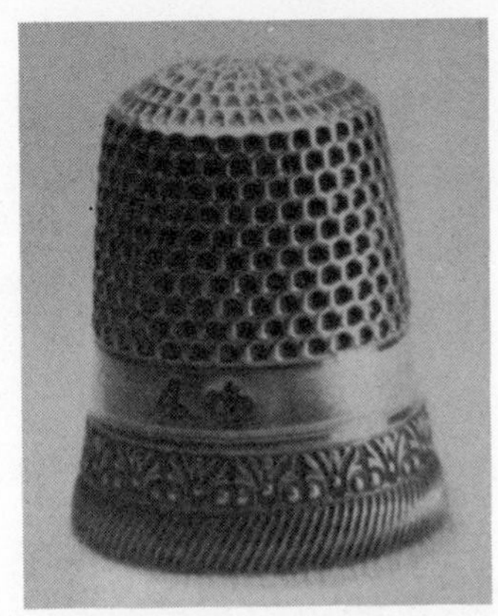
Sterling. Beaded palmate band; diagonal slashed rim; crown mark. (C)

Sterling. Tongue and dart band. Simons Bros. (C)

Sterling. Shield band. Simons Bros. (C)

Sterling. Feathers and dots band; beaded rim. Simons Bros. (C)

Sterling. Propeller band; diagonal slashed rim; anchor mark. (C)

Sterling. Oval shield band; slashed rim. Simons Bros. (C)

Sterling. Feathers band; feathers rim; star mark. (C)

Sterling. Ribbed band. (B)

Silver and Gold. Applied gold band with raised flowers. Simons Bros. (E)

Gilt over silver, Paris. Hallmarked. 1750. (F)

Silver with applied gold band. Feather band. C. 1890. (E)

Gold wash over silver (vermeil), France. Second to third quarter nineteenth century. (F)

Silver with applied gold. Geometric floral. C. 1900. (E)

Sterling top, applied gold band. Crown mark; inscribed "A.M.P." C. 1890. (E)

Silver and Gold. Applied gold band with paneled shields and leaves. Simons Bros. (E)

Silver and Gold. Applied gold band with raised shields. Simons Bros. (E)

Sterling top, applied gold band and panels. Anchor mark. C. 1890. (E)

Silver and Gold. Applied gold band with fancy triangles. Simons Bros. (E)

Silver with applied gold band. Paneled band. C. 1890. (E)

Silver with applied gold band. Paneled band; crown mark. C. 1890. (E)

Sterling top, applied gold band, ribs, and panels. Simons Bros. C. 1890. (E)

Silver with applied gold band. Feathered panels. C. 1890. (E)

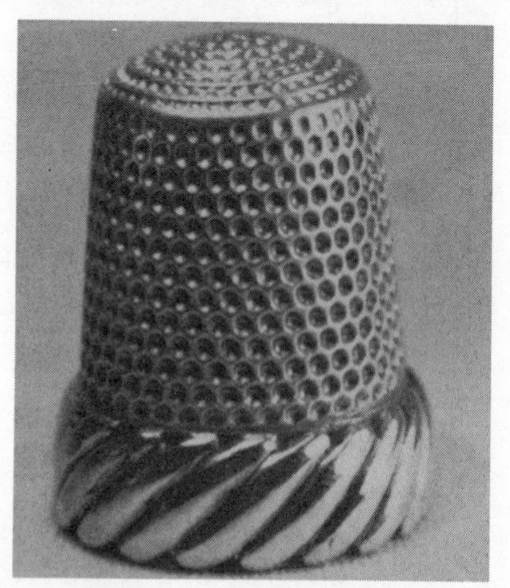

Sterling top, applied gold band. Rope design. Simons Bros. C. 1890. (E)

Silver with applied gold band. Reeding and panels. Simons Bros. C. 1890. (E)

Silver with applied gold. band. Quaker band. C. 1890. (E)

WATERLOO

Silver and gold. Sterling top; gold letters, "Waterloo." (D)

23 ESKIMO TOOLS

THE Eskimo used thimbles that they made differently according to their locality and the materials that were available at the time a new thimble was needed. Usually they were small, oval pieces of tough sealskin that had a slit extending across one edge. With this slit, a loop-like strap was formed, through which the forefinger was thrust. The thimble was then arranged in such a manner that the strap rested across the nail and the pad of sealskin on the inner side of the finger.

When traders introduced metal thimbles to the Eskimos, they preferred to continue using the sealskin type that they had used for many generations. They sewed the metal thimbles onto strips of cloth and used them as ornamental jingling bells. The shape of the metal thimble, however, was sometimes copied—the men carved it out of ivory.

The Eskimo woman carried her thimble on a holder at the end of a hook-shaped cord, which was fastened to her workbag or attached as a pendant to the strap of her needlecase. These thimble holders varied in shape and design. One of the earliest and crudest was made from a plain piece of bone taken from the leg of a bird. Others were made of ivory in different shapes. Hooks were made from walrus teeth and also from deer horn. One example from Nunivak Island is carved in the shape of a salmon.

24 THIMBLES PLUS

DURING the history of the thimble, it has been combined with numerous other objects and had other uses. In the late 1700s, some thimbles were made to screw on to a rounded silver base, on which was mounted a miniature scent bottle. One example had an open filigree band and covered a bottle of blue Bristol glass. Many of these thimble-scent-bottle combinations had a crest or monogram engraved under the base. This was used during the then common practice of a woman pressing her thimble into the hot wax, with which letters were sealed. The crest or monogram could also have been engraved on the dome of the thimble.

Thimbles sometimes screwed on to various items, such as a pair of scissors or a stilletto, for which it formed a base. A thimble could also screw on to a chatelaine. Thread lines may be found on the inside of the base in some thimbles. Many fit on to a small etui or a base that held pins and needles. One was even found that screwed on to a corkscrew.

Another dual-use thimble has been called the "secret" or "poison" thimble. These may have originated either in France or in Italy. These have a loose top that can be opened to reveal a small inner compartment situated just under the dome of the thimble. This tiny space could have held a secret message or a rendezvous to keep with a lover; or perhaps a tiny sweet in case the needlewoman became hungry during her work. The thin glass might have covered a portrait of her love or perhaps some poison that would be available upon breaking the glass with pressure.

Thimbles were used for a dual purpose in doing a type of quilting called thimble quilting. The thimble was used as finger protection in the normal manner; however, it also served as a quilting pattern. The thimble was put on the background of the quilt top and traced around the rim. This made a small circle. These thimble-sized circles were closely grouped on the fabric so that a pattern of dot-like shapes was formed. When the quilt top was quilted through the batting and backing material, the quilter used very small stitches to go around this traced design. Thus, the finished quilt had a background pattern of a great many small circles, each the size of the thimble's circumference.

Metal. Single thread cutter and band. (B)

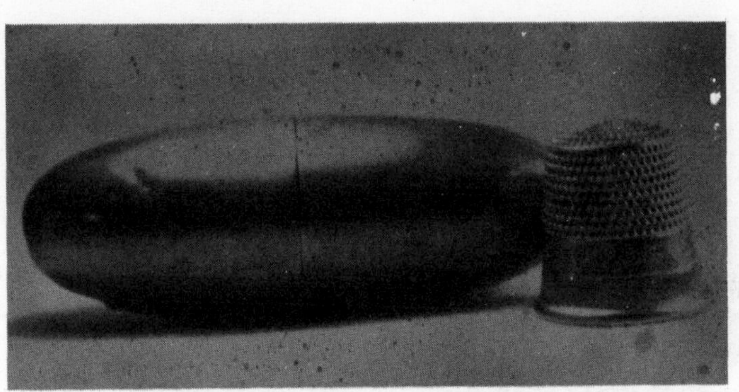

Sewing kit with thimble–sterling; F + B mark. (E)

White metal–size 10, "PAT'D made in U.S.A."–has thread cutter and needle threader device on side. (B)

Sewing kit. Plastic, green; set with rhinestones, green silk tassels; thread spools and needle case inside. (D)

Sewing kit. Copper with enamel; orange with pink roses and green leaves–Germany. Three reels for thread and needle case inside. (F)

Sewing kit. Plastic–France. Blue thimble hat, head covers thread, scissors, and needles inside; pink ribbon bow. (C)

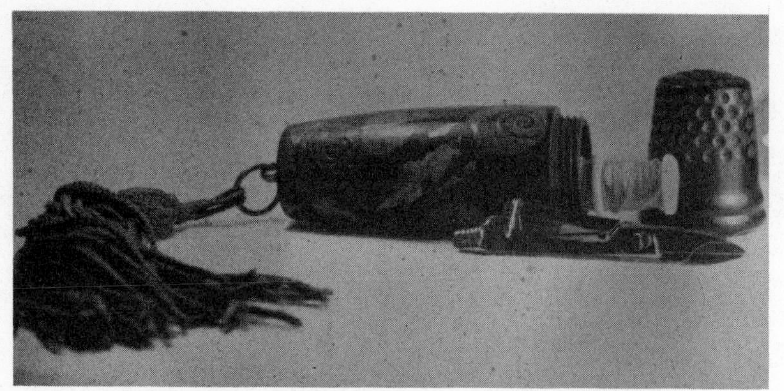

Sewing kit. Celluloid. Black with hand-painted red roses and green leaves, red silk tassle, "Dergee" on bottom. Scissors, thread, and needle inside. (D)

Sewing kit. Sterling and enamel moonstone-top thimble; blue and white windmill scenes; scissors, thread reels, and needle case inside; blue tassel. (F)

Sewing kit. Bakelite–France. Thimble top, thread spools, and needle case inside. (C)

Sewing kit. Celluloid–Germany. Orange; thread spools and needle case inside. (C)

Sewing kit. Celluloid–Germany. Red orange with black geometric design; dark red tassel; thread spool and needle case inside. (C)

Sewing kit. Brass–Germany. Lavender band with Greek key design; thread, spools and needle case inside. (D)

Sewing kit. Brass with green enamel–Germany. Brass, three-tiered thimble; wooden thread spool and needle case inside. (C)

Sewing kit. Steel case, brass thimble. "Lydia Pinkham's Vegetable Compound Blood Medicine Sanative Wash Liver Pills." (D)

Sewing kit. Brass and enamel–Germany. Bright red; wooden thread spool and needle case inside. (C)

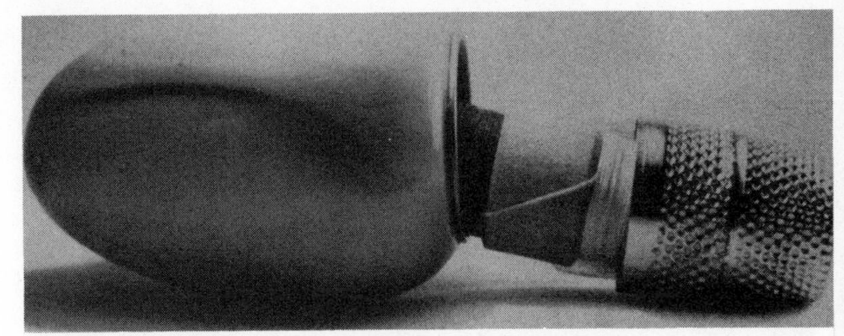

Sewing kit. Wood with enamel; brass thimble–Germany. Pink background with blue and red swirls; wooden thread reels and needle case inside. (C)

Sewing Kit with Thimble. Wood. Painted with lady wearing green collar. (D)

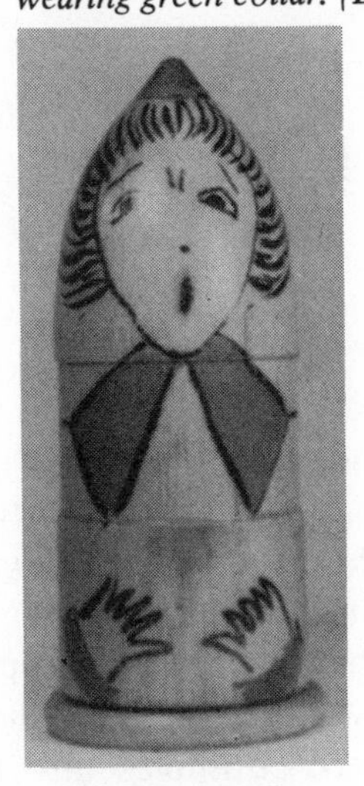

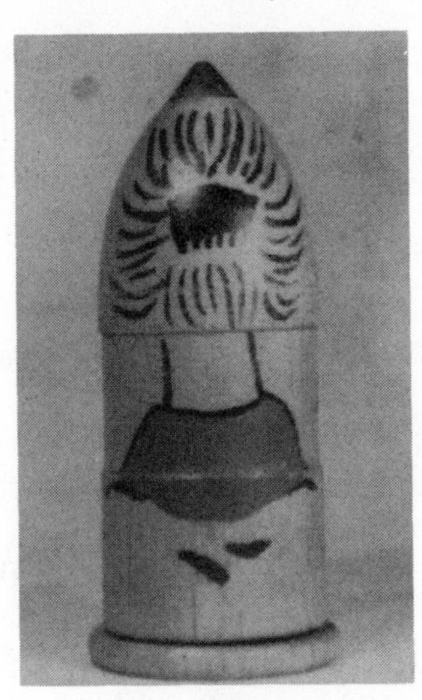

Back of case.

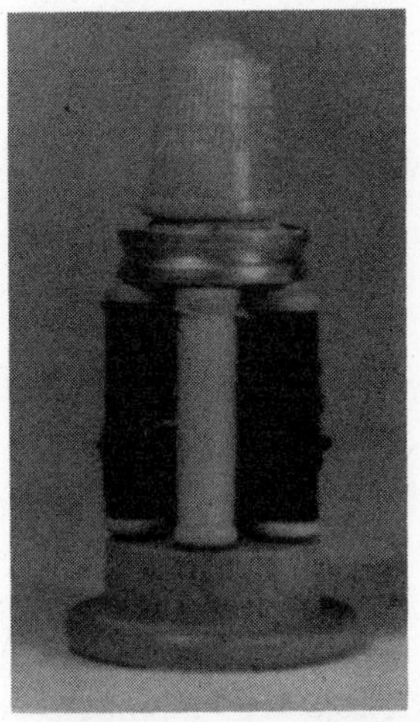

Inside of case showing blue plastic thimble (size 8) and five spools of black and white thread.

Sewing Kit with Thimble. Wood. "PICCADILLY Combination Sewing Needle Case" on back - "Portland, Me." Contains aluminum thimble, pins, needles, black and white thread. (C)

Sewing kit. Plush and brass thimble–England. Red and gold plush, brass corners and catch; spools of red, purple, brown, and tan thread; packet of needles; 5/9 Sharps: "John James and Sons, Redditch Crystal Packet, 5/9 Sharps." (C)

25 THIMBLE CASES AND HOLDERS

MANY special thimbles deserve and have special cases to hold them. Thimble holders have been known for centuries. The earlier ones seemed to have been made for the more exclusive members of society who could afford them. Perhaps the tradition of giving thimbles as gifts led to the development of small ornamental holders for them. This made the thimble a doubly pleasing present for the lady to receive.

During the end of the eighteenth century and the beginning of the nineteenth, thimbles to be presented as gifts were often enclosed in small cases made of precious metals. Some of these cases were just big enough for the thimble alone. Others were bigger. They were designed with places for needles and pins, the thimble, and often thread. Some even had a place for a small pair of scissors.

In sixteenth-century France, goldsmiths and silversmiths were making thimbles in precious metals and setting many kinds of jewels into them. These fancy thimbles were usually provided with a matching case or casket. During this same period of time English thimbles were very simple in decoration, and their holders, if any, were likewise simple in design and decoration. An inventory of possessions of the King of Navarre, made in 1583, included a listing of little gold thimbles set with rubies, housed in their own little black leather caskets.

Queen Elizabeth I of England apparently owned "a nedel case of cristall, garnished with silver-gilt, with two thimbles in it." An indented but unornamented plain gold thimble is among her personal possessions now kept at Burghley House, which is near Stamford, England. But the crystal holder is no longer in existence.

Historical items such as these can be seen in museums. But the collector of today is most likely to find cases from the eighteenth or nineteenth century. A large variety of materials was used. They were formed into an almost endless variety of shapes; thus, this relatively short span of time produced many choice examples of the thimble case to be collected.

A partial list of the materials used includes the following: horn, ivory, vegetable ivory (corozo nut), polished woods, Turnbridge ware, glass, leather, tortoiseshell, china, and shagreen. Shagreen originally was untanned leather from the hide of a horse or wild ass obtained from Persia and Turkey. During the seventeenth century, shagreen was made artificially by pressing small seeds into skins while they were soft and flexible. They became firm after they were dyed green or black and dried. Still later, shagreen was made by polishing the skins of seals, sharks, and other fish.

Fancier thimble cases were made of agates, marbles, and jades that were decorated with gold, silver, and enamels. The Imperial Court of Russia provided a sense of luxury that was clearly displayed by the small Easter-egg type caskets, which the ladies of the court used to hold their thimbles. Some of the most beautiful ones were made by Carl Fabergé and his workmen. These were enamelled in a wide range of unusual colors and were also richly ornamented with silver and gold tracery. Many were also set with precious stones. These were typical of the fabulous Fabergé period of design. Chelsea-enamelled thimbles frequently were housed in matching enamelled cases.

Ivory holders in the shape of an egg sometimes had naturalistic paintings. In the eighteenth century these were sometimes covered with a fine design fashioned of beadwork.

The shapes of fruits or nuts were often used for thimble cases. Popular ones were walnuts, acorns, strawberries, apples, carrots, and eggs. The carrot-shaped one could have had an emery cushion, used for sharpening needles, on a screw-on lid. Some of the cases with these shapes stand on a lathe-turned base.

Another kind of case was the octagonal box that was veneered with tortoiseshell or mother-of-pearl. This one was similar in appearance to the needlecase with sloping lid of the 1800s. Some of this type were large enough to store graduated packets of needles as well as the thimble.

A popular case from the Victorian age is the miniature brass-bound trunk that is covered with velvet. Leather ones were also made. These were usually lined with silk, plush, or both. Other shapes were also made of leather. One the author has, which shows great imagination, is shaped like a tophat carrying case. The crown part lifts off the brim part to reveal the upside-down thimble.

Other shapes include small barrels, eggcups, chalices, and simple cylindrical or even square boxes. In the middle of the 1800s many thimbles came in small caskets similar to ring boxes. Basket shapes were made of fine wickerware or carved realistically from wood.

People in the Victorian age loved souvenirs. Thimble cases made a pleasant rememberance to buy or receive as a gift. These souvenir cases were usually made of highly polished light wood and had a black-and-white picture on the lid. This picture would depict the place where the case was bought. An American example of such a case pictures the monument at Bunker Hill. English examples include Gloucester Cathedral, Glastonbury Tor, Osborne House, and many other vacation spots. Some of these souvenir cases contained a yard measure, emery or wax-holder, as well as the thimble.

In this era, stores often displayed thimbles for sale in cases or boxes that were covered on the outside with lithographed paper and lined on the inside with cloth. Because the storekeeper usually threw away these cases after the thimbles they held were sold, such cases are now scarce and are a real find for the collector.

A separate collectible item that can, among its other uses, serve as a thimble holder is a chatelaine. A chatelaine is a brooch or clasp from which is suspended a number of items by means of chains, one for each item. The chatelaine was worn at the waist by the eighteenth-century woman. Originally it held a watch and was worn by both men and women, but the type of interest to the thimble collector was worn by a woman. Most of the objects that were hung from the hook-plate by means of the chains had a useful purpose. The average number of items ranged from three to five. Included among the common were a nutmeg grater, earspoons, tweezers, tongue-scrapers, toothpicks, lancets, knives, pencils, memo books, matchbox, patch box, powder box, mirror, stamp box, small purses, pomander, button hook, a dog whistle, and sewing items. The sewing items are pin cushion, needlecase, scissors in a scissors sheath, bodkin case, emery, and, of course, thimble in a thimble holder. Many of the chatelaines were of silver or silver plate, but some were of gold or other precious metals or of other base metals.

The thimble-holder part of the chatelaine was often of a bucket shape. Many of the silver cases found in the collector's hunt may be found to have a small ring on it. This ring was the means of attaching the case to the chain.

It is somewhat unusual to find a chatelaine today that has all of its original parts intact. Also, to find the thimble holder with the original thimble in it is a treat for the collector.

One of the reasons why the chatelaine lost its popularity was the advent of the age of machines and mass production. The hanging objects were too much of a safety hazard to be practical when women helped production at a time that the world got caught in war.

Another device that was not strictly a thimble case but was often used to carry a thimble so it would always be near at hand was the quilted pocket of the eighteenth century. It was often used in the Dutch colonies including New Amsterdam and was sometimes called a "Dutch Housewife." This was a fairly large pocket made of quilted material, often the never-discarded scraps from other projects. It was shaped somewhat like a rectangle and was composed of a top and bottom piece joined on all four sides. There was a slit, with bound edges, vertically in the middle of the top piece through which the items were placed inside. This pocket was worn tied around the waist by the woman of the period. It was very useful for keeping handy sewing utensils such as needles, pins, scissors, thimble, thread, and bodkin, and other items the woman was likely to use frequently during her busy day while keeping house. Quilting was used for strength because scissors are heavy and needles and pins are sharp. This device was necessary because ladies' skirts at that time were not made with pockets included in the construction of the garment. Some sources state that the pocket was worn under the skirt. This would seem very awkward, as the main purpose was to keep the items carried in it easily accessible. It seems more probable that the pocket was worn over the skirt and quickly and easily removed if company arrived or another sort of interruption caused the woman to want to have less of a "I am at work" appearance.

This type of pocket was worn until the high waist and slim lines of the Empire-style dress became fashionable at the turn of the nineteenth century.

A Delaware resident, Mrs. A. Ridgely, in a letter she wrote to her son in 1796, told him of her visit with a young French lady:

> A young lady visited here last week who profess'd herself "astonished to find your sisters at work," and declared in a sweet simper, that she never had sizars, thimble, needle or thread about her, for it was a terrible in a lady to wear a pair of Pockets—the French Ladies never did such a thing. What can such a poor vain piece of affectation and folly be worth? Nothing—and if she possess'd the wealth of the Indies and I was a man I would scarcely even pay her the compliment of a word.

Thimble case. Sterling; walnut-shaped, ring for chatelaine. (F)

Thimble case. Sterling; round box, pierced sides; thimble sits on post; inscribed on top "E.V.N." Webster Company. (F)

Thimble case. Sterling; top slides up chains; red velvet lining, figure finial. (G)

Thimble case. Acorn shape, ring for chatelaine. (F)

Thimble case. Leather brown; brass hinge and clasp, lined with white silk and white velvet. (D)

Thimble. Sterling; silver lace design. (F)

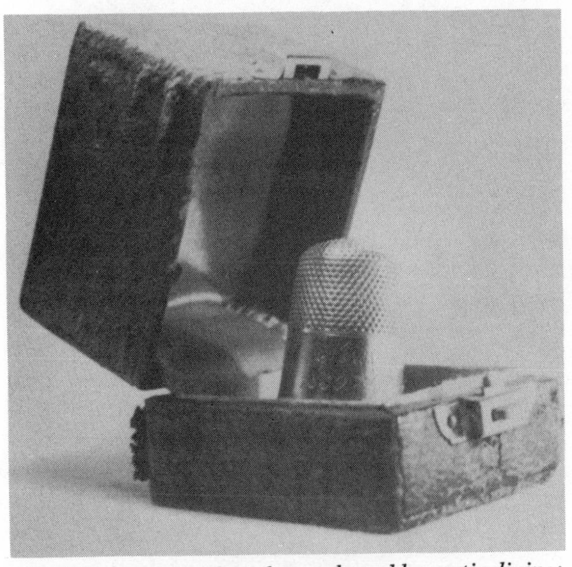

Thimble case. Leather; brass clasp, blue satin lining: "H.T. Joreoki, Erie, Pa." 1889. (D)

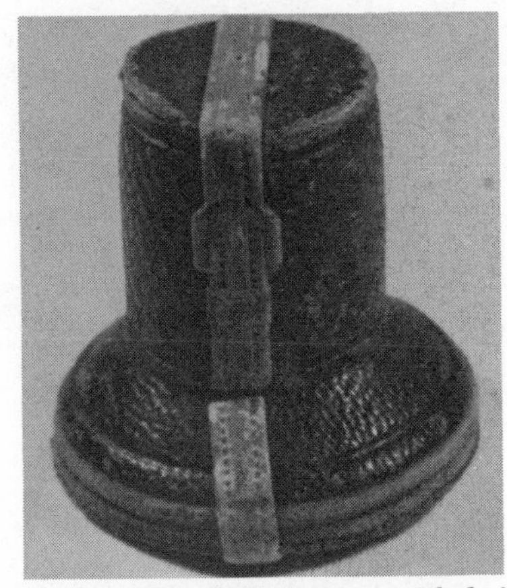

Thimble case. Leather; dark brown with beige strap buckle decoration embossed on it. Thimble sits upside-down under crown part. (E)

Thimble case. Leather, dark red, brass clasp; lined in dark blue velvet, white satin. (D)

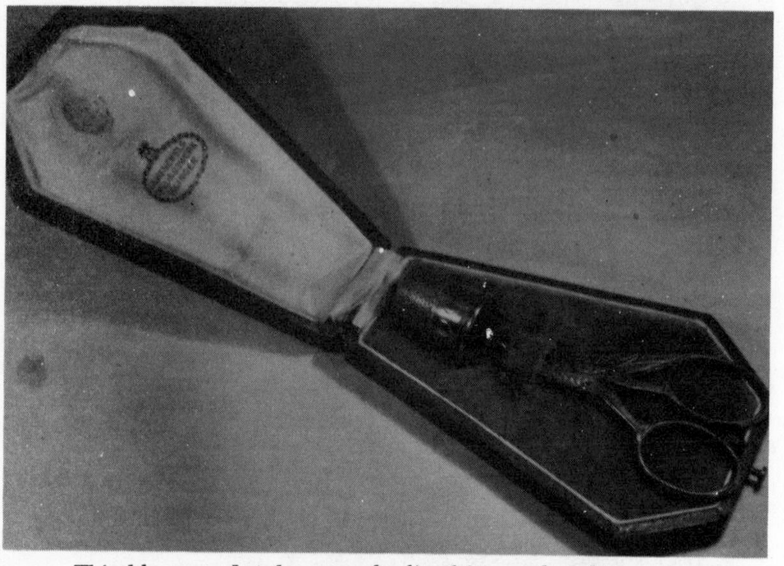

Thimble case. Leather, purple, lined in purple velvet and white satin: "J.A. Henckels Zwillingswerk Solingen"; holds thimble and scissors. (D)

Thimble case. Gold leaf on metal; beveled glass window on top; blue velvet inside. (E)

Thimble case. Sweetgrass basket; part of a set. (C)

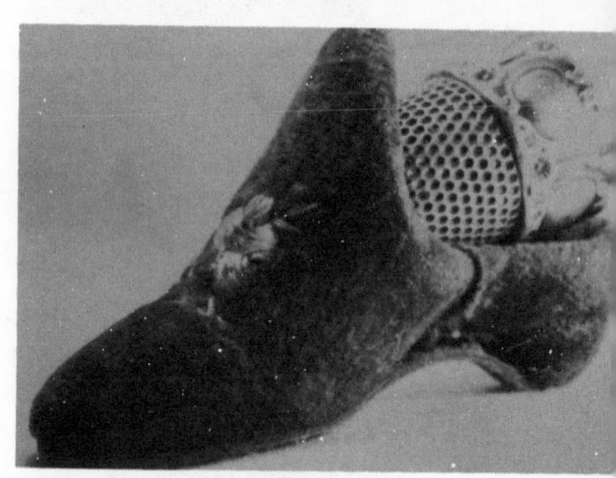

Thimble case. Slipper shape; purple velvet with pink embroidered flower on toe. (D)

Thimble case. Shoe shape; wood, carved design on toe. (D)

Thimble case. Wood; Tunbridge ware; black, dark brown, medium brown, and beige woods. (E)

Thimble case—Chinese. Embroidered silk, white background, bird and flower designs, orange tassel, silver thread decoration. (D)

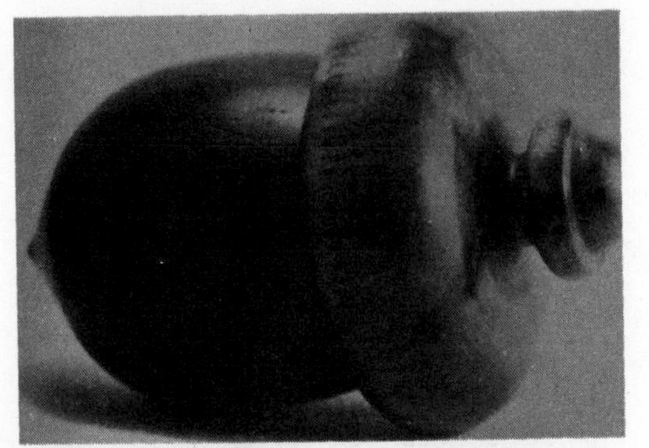

Thimble case. Olive wood, acorn shape; gold velvet in top. (E)

Thimble case. Ivory, carved in high relief showing men, pagodas, and vegetation from China. (E)

Thimble case. Wood, nut-shaped, hand-carved. (D)

Thimble case. Vegetable ivory; red stain on one side makes very realistic apple-type coloring. (F)

Thimble case. Cardboard and paper cherub on top; blue flowers and green leaves on sides; labels inside: "H.C. Jedeloo + Zonen Hof-Juweliers, Van H.M. de Konongin Delft Markt, Telefoon 276." (D)

Thimble case. Vegetable ivory; hand-carved; unscrew in middle. (E)

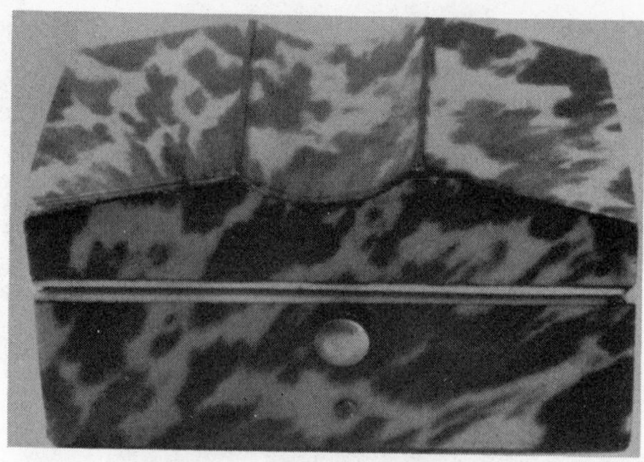

Thimble case–circa 1800-1820. Tortoiseshell, maroon velvet, and satin interior, with room for three thimbles; came from the western part of England. (F)

Thimble case. Vegetable ivory. Unscrews in the middle - thimble inside. (E)

Thimble case. Mother-of-pearl on ivory; tortoiseshell base, lined in red velvet; post to hold thimble; space at back for package of needles; circa 1800. (G)

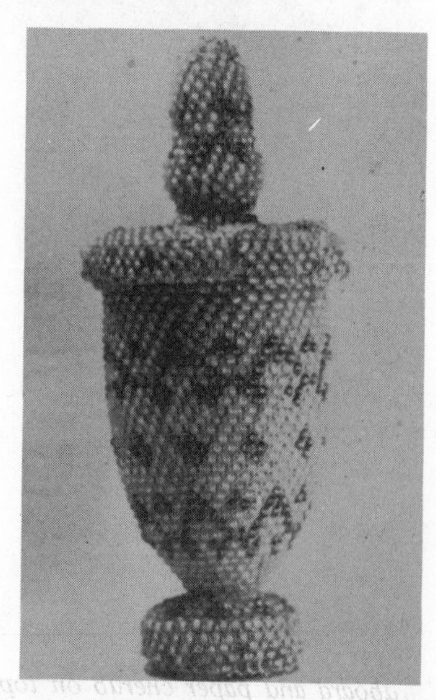

Thimble case–France. Beads over ivory; pale blue, green, dark red, and gold. Top unscrews; needle case in top; circa 1780. (H)

Thimble holder. Celluloid. Marked "DRP No 86621" Dark red velvet stand to hold thimble. Girl in Regency-style dress holding wand. (D)

Thimble holder. Alabaster. Red, blue, and yellow painted flowers. "A Present from Niagara Falls." Thimble sits on a post on the inside. (D)

Chatelaine. Silver plate; hook plate has four chains holding pincushion (red velvet); chalk holder; scissors sheath; thimble bucket (lined with red velvet). (H)

Thimble holder. Shell and metal. Bisque sailor boy sitting on shell boat with flowers painted on the shell sail. (E)

Set of sewing items. Sterling; fleur-de-lis design; needle case with red leather; thimble and thread cases. (G)

Shell (mother-of-pearl) bisque figure–brass–1890-1900. (G)

Set of sewing items. Sweetgrass. Silk basket, thimble case, scissors sheath, pincushion with green velvet. (F)

Sewing box. Wood; cut-steel nailheads; mother-of-pearl decorations; circa 1780, France. (J)

Sewing box. Inside showing mirror in lid; white satin cushion; red and white trim.

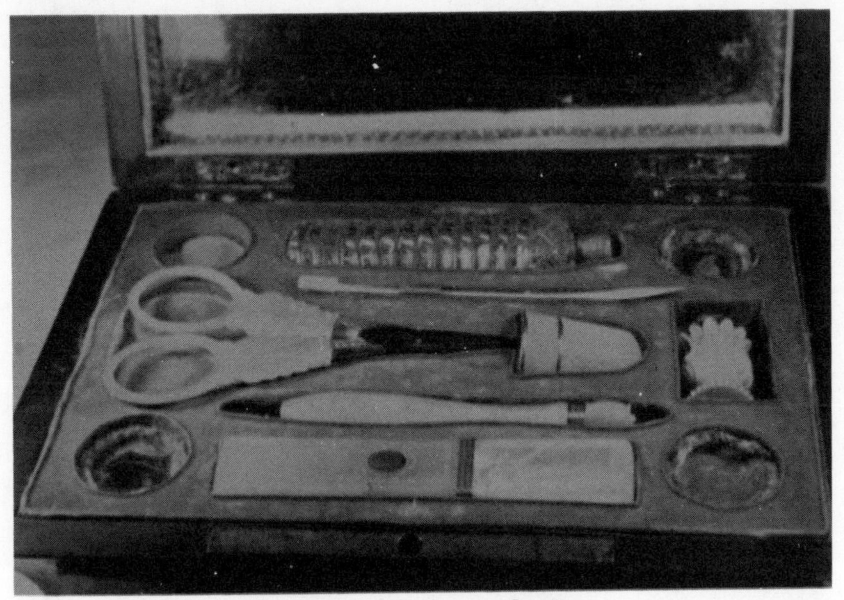

Sewing box. Inside–satin cushion removea. Implements (from front): red-lined tray; needle case–mother-of-pearl and gold; crochet hook–mother-of-pearl and gold; scissors–m.o.p. and gold; thimble–m.o.p. and gold; emory cushion–ivory and red velvet; bodkin–ivory; scent bottle–cut glass.

Sewing box. Leather (black); gold stamping: "Lady's Companion"; contains mirror, leather needle book, scent vial, stiletto, sterling thimble; circa 1860. (E)

26 DISPLAY TECHNIQUES

A thimble collection is wonderful for many reasons. Besides the joy of the thimbles themselves as works of art and as historical objects, they are also practical as collectible items. A thimble is small, and a great number can be stored in a small amount of space. In the smaller houses and apartments where so many people live today, storage space sometimes dictates the items a person collects.

There are numerous attractive ways to store and display a thimble collection. New ideas are constantly being thought of. A few of the more popular ones include antique thread cases, small-parts cabinets that are easily obtainable at hardware stores, and display boards. Commercial display boards with a number of pegs at about a forty-five-degree angle can be bought. One thimble sits on top of each peg. A homemade version of this idea would consist of a board covered with velvet. Small nails would be driven into the wood and then bent up so the thimble would slip over it and be held upright against the velvet. The board could then be hung on the wall.

A good place for a beginner to keep his collection is a small-parts cabinet. These have a number of plastic drawers, each of which can hold numerous thimbles. Different types of thimbles can be kept in different drawers. The outside of the cabinet can be covered with a pretty fabric to take away the commercial look.

One of the most interesting ways to display a collection of antique thimbles is in something antique. One example could be an old tray used to hold printer's type. These trays have numerous shallow compartments of varying sizes. When hung on the wall, the thimbles appear to sit in the compartments as if on shelves.

Another idea in the use of antiques is the thread case formerly seen in the old general store. One type of these cases had two or more drawers with the thread company's name on them. Careful hunting can bring forth other styles, also. One the author has is covered with mirrors on three sides. The company names are above and below the mirrors. The drawers—there are five—have glass fronts. Each pulls out to reveal 125 pegs upon which the spools of thread sat. Each peg holds one thimble very nicely.

A third idea is a cabinet having a mirror back and glass sides and a glass door. There are three glass shelves. This case was probably used originally as an instrument case in a doctor's office or maybe in a barber shop. Now it holds some of the larger thimble cases and a chatelaine and sewing bird.

Thimble-advertising piece. Pewter, unmarked. Used as a display by shop that sold thimbles. 2¼ inches high, 1¾ inches across base. Note pouncing of circles alternating with rows of small slash marks; circa 1860.

White metal. Advertising display piece. Shows Simons Brothers Co. trade mark. Fifteen inches high.

Display case. Antique; one of a pair. Lighted picture frame, three glass shelves, black velvet back, white frame, holds thimble cases. (E)

Display case. Antique barber's case. Glass sides and door, mirror back, three shelves, holds larger items. (F)

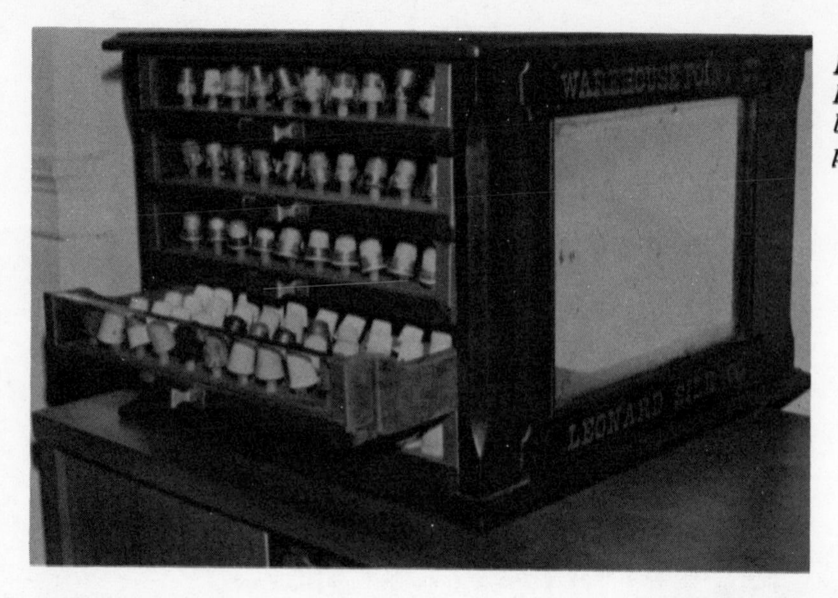

Display case. Antique spool cabinet. "Warehouse Point CT, Leonard Silk Co." Black walnut, glass, brass drawer pulls. Three mirrors, five drawers–120 pegs in each. (I)

Display case. Antique type tray. Originally held printer's type; eighty-nine compartments of different sizes. (E)

Display case. Modern. Steel and plastic small parts cabinet; twenty-five drawers, covered with calico and braid. (C)

27 PHOTOGRAPHS

ANOTHER hobby that the author enjoys pursuing is photography. The thimble collection and photography became logical partners when the need for identification of individual thimbles arose. The original idea was identification for insurance purposes. The idea grew when requests for the author to give lectures on her collection were received. This posed a problem of logistics. How to be able to show the thimbles, which are very small, to a group of people in such a way that they could easily see the details that were being talked about was remedied by 135 mm color slides. When projected on a screen they were large enough for all present to see clearly. An added benefit was the protection from possible theft. The actual thimbles, which could be slipped into a pocket or purse so easily, were not needed at the lecture, so they could be left in safety.

The next problem became one of technique. How to produce clear, detailed slides of objects that small was puzzling. After many unsuccessful trials a workable setup was found. A Canon single lens reflex camera, model FTB, with a 50 mm 1.8 lens with a +10 close-up attachment on it was used. This was set up firmly on a steady tripod and a cable release was used. A small table was used to hold the thimbles and their fabric background. The lighting that worked the best turned out to be a pair of ordinary high-intensity desk lamps, one used for side lighting and the other for front lighting. A white reflector was put up opposite the side lamp to lessen the heavy shadows.

For the color slides, Kodak High Speed Ektachrome type B film was used. For the black-and-white shots, Kodak Plus X film was used. The ASA number of both films is 125. The lens was set at f16 to give the most depth of field possible. This allowed for maximum sharpness within the small focus range of the close-up attachment. The f stop had priority so the shutter speed was adjusted to fit the exposure needs of the individual thimbles. This combination produced well-lighted, detailed slides and pictures of each individual thimble.

For the larger items, such as cases and sewing kits, a close-up set with +1 +2, and +4 attachments was used. These three can be combined to work as attachments with strengths of +1 through +7. The combination used varied in indirect relation to the size of the object being photographed. The larger the object, the smaller the number of the attachment used. This arrangement turned out to be very satisfactory.

BIBLIOGRAPHY

Andere, Mary. *Old Needlework Boxes and Tools.* New York: Drake Publishers Ltd., 1971.

Burgess, Fred W. *Antique Jewelry and Trinkets.* New York: Tudor Publishing Co., 1937.

Butler, Joseph T. *American Antiques 1800-1900.* New York: Odyssey Press, 1965.

Caulfield, S. and Saward, B. *The Dictionary of Needlework.* London: 1882 (original), New York: Arno Press, 1972 (copy).

Clayton, Michael. *The Collector's Dictionary of the Silver and Gold of Great Britain and North America.* New York: World Publishing Co., 1971.

Cole, Ann Kilborn. *Antiques–How to Identify, Buy, Sell, Refinish, and Care For Them.* New York: David McKay Co., Inc., 1957.

Eberlein, H.D. and McClure, A. *The Practical Book of American Antiques.* Philadelphia: J.B. Lippincott Co., 1927.

Groves, Sylvia. *The History of Needlework Tools and Accessories.* New York: Arco Publishing Co., Inc., 1973.

Hanley, Hope. *Needlepoint in America.* New York: Charles Scribner's Sons, 1969.

Harbeson, Georgiana Brown. *American Neddlework.* New York: Coward-McCann, Inc., 1938.

Hughes, G. Bernard. *Small Antique Silverware.* New York: Bramhall House, 1957.

Hume, Ivor Noel. *A Guide to Artifacts of Colonial America.* New York: Alfred A. Knopf, 1970.

Kauffman, Henry J. *The Colonial Silversmith–His Technique and His Products.* Camden, N.J.: Thomas Nelson, Inc., 1969.

Kovel, Ralph and Terry. *Know Your Antiques.* New York: Crown Publishers, Inc., 1967.

Lundquist, Myrtle. *The Book of a Thousand Thimbles.* Des Moines, Iowa: Wallace-Homestead Book Co., 1970.

Mebane, John. *The Coming Collecting Boom.* Cranbury, N.J.: A.S. Barnes and Co., Inc., 1968.

McClinton, Katharine M. *The Complete Book of Small Antiques Collecting.* New York: Coward-McCann, Inc., 1965.

Negus, Arthur. *Discovering Antiques–The Story of World Antiques.* New York: Greystone Press.

Orlofsky, Patsy and Myron. *Quilts in America.* New York: McGraw-Hill Book Co., 1974.

Phipps, Frances. *Collector's Complete Dictionary of American Antiques.* Garden City, N.Y.: Doubleday and Co., Inc., 1974.

Rainwater, Dorothy T. *Encyclopedia of American Silver Manufacturers.* New York: Crown Publishers, Inc., 1975.

Sterling Silversmiths Guild of America. *The Story of Sterling.*

Whiting, Gertrude. *Old-Time Tools and Toys of Needlework.* New York: Dover Publications, Inc., 1971.

Williams, Carl M. *Silversmiths of New Jersey 1700-1825.* Philadelphia: George S. MacManus Co., 1949.

MAGAZINES

"New Delvings in Old Fields." *Antiques,* XX: 3, September 1931, pp. 176-180.

"The History of Sewing Tools"–part IV: "Hunt the Thimble." *Embroidery,* Spring 1963, pp. 28-29.

Howell, Dorothy. "Collecting Thimbles." *Antique Dealer and Collector's Guide,* 1:10, May 1965, pp. 48-50.

Illustrated London News, 3 December 1949, p. 842.

Illustrated London News, 23 August 1958, p. 300.

Shaffer, Sandra C. "Sewing Tools in the Collection of Colonial Williamsburg." *Antiques,* August 1973, pp. 233-241.

Sickles, Elizabeth Galbraith. "Thimblemakers in America." *Antiques,* September 1967.

____. "New York Thimble Makers from Huntington, Long Island, Part I." *The Antiques Journal,* 19:9, September 1964, pp. 13-17.

____. "New York Thimble Makers from Huntington, Long Island, Part II." *The Antiques Journal,* 19:10, October 1964, pp. 18-23.

____. "New York Thimble Makers from Huntington, Long Island, Part III." *The Antiques Journal,* 19:11 November 1964, pp. 21-26.

Smith, Marilyn Estes. "Thimbles to Collect." *Spinning Wheel,* 28:3, April 1972, pp. 12-15.

The Sewing Corner. Whitestone, N.Y., 1975.

INDEX